Franco Columbu's Complete Book of Bodybuilding

Franco Columbu's Complete Book of Bodybuilding

Dr. Franco Columbu

Contemporary Books, Inc.
Chicago

Library of Congress Cataloging in Publication Data

Columbu, Franco.
Franco Columbu's complete book of bodybuilding.

Includes index.
1. Bodybuilding. 2. Physical fitness. 3. Nutrition.
I. Title. II. Title: Complete book of bodybuilding.
GV546.5.C64 646.7'5 81-69606
ISBN 0-8092-5984-2 AACR2
ISBN 0-8092-5983-4 (pbk.)

The majority of the photographs in this book were taken by Art Zeller. Other photographers include: John Balik, Albert Busek, Richard Ortiz, Bill Dobbins, Jimmy Caruso, George Butler, Benno Dahmen *(Athletic Sport Journal)*, George Rodriquez, and Robert Gardner.

Published by Contemporary Books, Inc.
180 North Michigan Avenue, Chicago, Illinois 60601
Manufactured in the United States of America
Library of Congress Catalog Card Number: 81-69606
International Standard Book Number: 0-8092-5984-2 (cloth)
0-8092-5983-4 (paper)

Published simultaneously in Canada by
Beaverbooks, Ltd.
150 Lesmill Road
Don Mills, Ontario M3B 2T5
Canada

To my good friends:
George Lois
Nick Masiello
Ben Weider
Joe Weider

I would like to thank Arnold Schwarzenegger
for his assistance throughout my career.

Contents

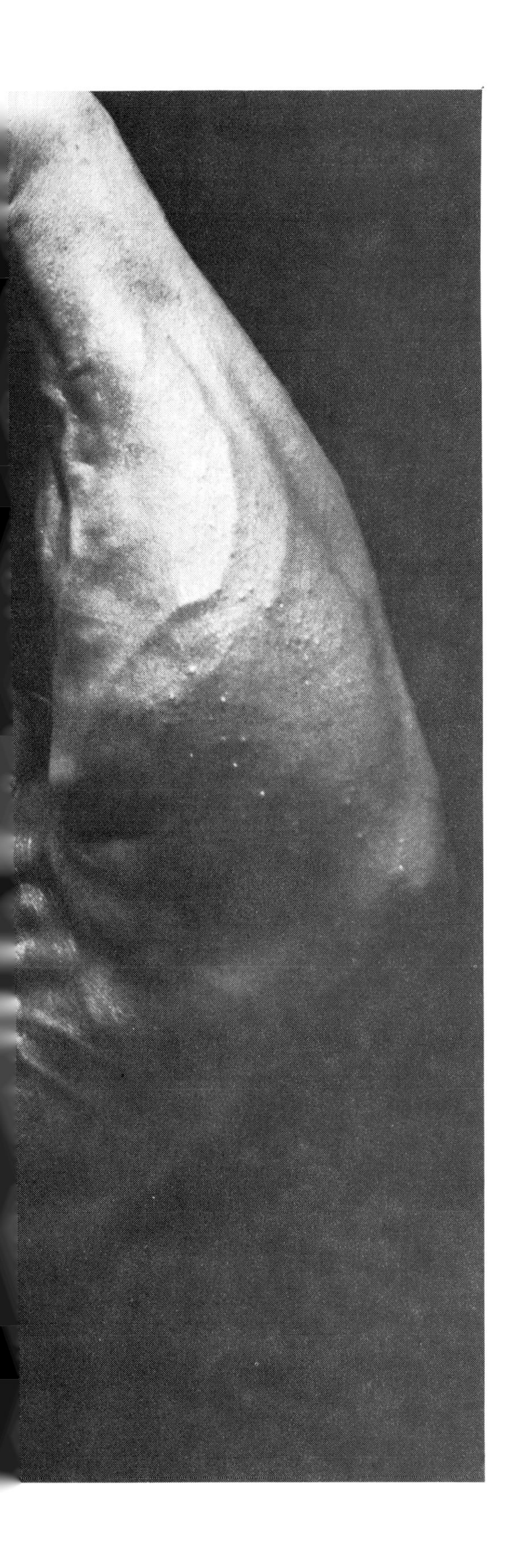

Foreword

by Arnold Schwarzenegger

Dr. Franco Columbu is one of the most remarkable men I have ever met. He is also, I am proud to say, one of my very closest friends.

We first met in Stuttgart, Germany, in 1965. I had come from Austria to compete in the European Bodybuilding Championships, and Franco from Italy for the powerlifting contest being held at the same time. As two foreigners, we got to talking and immediately hit it off.

A couple of years later, Franco and I wound up training in the same gym in Munich. In 1967, I won my first Mr. Universe title. Afterwards, Franco came up to me and surprised me by saying, "Arnold, I want to do the same thing. I want to become Mr. Universe."

There were a lot of people around the gym who laughed at this idea. Certainly, Franco didn't look like Mr. Universe material back then. He was very strong, but his small stature and relative lack of development seemed to indicate he lacked the genetic potential to become a champion bodybuilder.

But I knew Franco well enough not to underestimate him. Once he makes up his mind to do something, he brings to bear a force of will that lets nothing stand in the way of reaching his goal. So we began to train together, and soon Franco was putting such enormous energy into his workouts that even I had trouble keeping up with him.

And all that work soon paid off. In 1970, only three years after Franco decided to switch from powerlifting to bodybuilding, he captured the Mr. Universe title. Almost overnight, he had made himself into one of the great bodybuilders of all time.

But Franco didn't accomplish this feat

Ben Weider, president of the International Federation of Bodybuilders (IFBB), congratulates Arnold on winning the Mr. Olympia title and Franco on winning the Mr. Universe title.

just by hard work alone. He had to learn to use all the resources of his mind as well as his body. For somebody like me, with a large bone structure and a 6′2″ frame, training has always been relatively easy. All I ever had to do was train, and the results came quickly.

For a bodybuilder like Franco, with a totally different kind of physical structure, this just wasn't enough. And so Franco learned about diet and nutrition, began using vitamin and mineral supplements long before it was common practice, and studied the way his body responded to different kinds of training programs.

Early on I could see that Franco had an interest in how the body worked that went far beyond my own. When we both came to live in the United States, I found myself more and more interested in business while Franco's desire to develop more understanding of the body led him to attend classes and seminars on nutrition, physiology, and kinesiology. While other bodybuilders spent hours lying around on the beach, Franco studied. And one day he came to me and announced, "I have decided what I want to do with my life. I want to become a Doctor of Chiropractic."

And that is just what he did. In 1976, Franco Columbu became a doctor of chiropractic. Soon he was swamped by body-

Before the 1981 Olympia, Arnold brings Franco a slice of pizza for energy and John Milius (director of CONAN THE BARBARIAN) asks if the pizza will make Franco look better for the contest.

builders seeking his help. They wanted to know what they could do to develop their bodies to the ultimate, how to diet, and what nutritional principles they should follow. And they came with all sorts of muscle pulls, strains, sprains, and training injuries that they wanted the Drs. Columbu to help them with.

The Columbu Chiropractic Center has continued to grow. At the same time, Franco has found the energy to combine his career in chiropractic with active participation in bodybuilding, and to write a series of books that make his special knowledge available to everyone.

Nowadays, there are any number of "experts" who are writing books on training and nutrition. But few of them can claim to speak with any real authority. However, Franco has the background of his chiropractic education, and constantly reviews research coming out of hospitals and laboratories all over the world. So when he tells you something, you know you can believe it.

Not only that, but Franco sees thousands of patients a year in his chiropractic practice, and he gets to observe the results of any physical or nutritional recommendation he might make. If there is anything that doesn't really work, he finds that out firsthand. And this constant dealing with reality is probably the best kind of research you can do.

All in all, I can think of nobody more impressive in his accomplishments than Dr. Franco Columbu. By the force of his own

Arnold and Franco (as a Pict warrior) on set of CONAN.

Arnold pushes Franco to do another grueling rep.

will, he has made himself into a champion in boxing, powerlifting, and bodybuilding. He came to this country with nothing, not even speaking the language, and now he is a doctor, an author, and a successful businessman.

Those of us who have come to this country from elsewhere are very conscious of what is called the "American Dream," the ability of an individual to make whatever he can of himself in this country, no matter where he comes from, his race, religion, or economic background. That is a very powerful idea, and I know of nobody who embodies it more completely than Franco.

A Horatio Alger story—from rags to riches. Franco Columbu is, indeed, a very special individual. And someone I am glad to call a very good friend.

Arnold Schwarzenegger

Preface

If you have just finished reading Arnold's Foreword, you know about my qualifications for writing this book. I would like to mention one other thing that should convince you that this book can guide you to achieve your personal health and fitness goals.

Several months after my first Mr. Olympia victory, my left knee was severely injured. No one who has not had a similar accident can imagine the pain—coupled with the mental anguish over possibly losing the use of a leg—that I suffered.

I was told that I could not compete again. However, I would not give up hope. Through my knowledge of corrective exercise along with therapy and chiropractic care, I was able to gradually place more and more stress on my injured leg. It took five long years to work myself into shape—better shape than I have ever been in before. And I won the 1981 Mr. Olympia by a greater margin than I did in 1976, and against a stronger field of competitors.

It is my desire that you will enrich your life and learn to maintain a healthy body and mind by studying the information in this book. I want you to achieve maximum results with your body in the least amount of time, which is the same goal for the competitive bodybuilder as it is for the noncompetitive bodybuilder.

I have included a basic training and nutrition program for the executive who has a limited amount of time to spend exercising (Chapter 1). In Chapters 2, 3, and 4, I have provided detailed information on equipment, anatomy, training schedules, training partners, attitude, exercise routines on many levels, and techniques and strategies for competition, posing, and sportsmanship—all for those who

seek to become bodybuilders at their own level of preference and performance.

I have prepared a brief, yet comprehensive, training program for female bodybuilders in Chapter 5.

For athletes who wish to improve their performance in other sports, I present specialized training routines and tips for over a dozen different sports in Chapter 6. And all athletes will want to learn about preventing and treating sports injuries covered in Chapter 7.

Because nutrition is such an essential part of bodybuilding and staying fit and healthy, I have devoted all of Chapter 8 to this subject. In fact, this chapter was so chock-full of information that my editors, for some reason, broke up my original manuscript so part of it appears in an appendix in the back of the book. For essential information on vitamins and minerals, you will need to look at the Appendix. Another part appears as Chapter 9, where I discuss the use of steroids and other drugs.

Finally, Chapter 10 will reiterate the important points to be found in this book. In that chapter, I will summarize the many benefits of bodybuilding that I and countless others have enjoyed, which I want to share with you.

So you won't have to flip through the

various chapters in this book on exercise routines, I have put together an Exercise Glossary on pages 121–186. It supplies photos of me performing each exercise in strict form and precise instructions on how to perform them.

And that is all. I have tried to provide something for everyone, to ensure that this is, indeed, the complete book of bodybuilding. I wish you the best: a strong body, a healthy mind, and a long, happy life.

Franco

Introduction

It is safe to assume that in prehistoric times only the strong survived, because it was the nature of the world. The survival of the fittest continued into recorded history. Whether king or slave, warrior or gladiator, the men of ancient times sought strong and muscular bodies through physical labor and physical combat and contests.

Now, the sport of bodybuilding is in its golden age. Millions of men (and women), in their search for fitness and exercise, have spurred manufacturers to develop new and efficient means of improving physical fitness. The trend toward physical fitness has caused a boom in industries developing weight resistance equipment. Professional and collegiate teams of every major sport have added compulsory weight regimens to their athletic programs. When it comes to training with weights and what it can do for your body and sports performance, today's real bodybuilding experts know volumes and volumes more than did authorities of earlier days.

What history tells us about bodybuilding—and it certainly remains true today—is that its best practitioners were men accustomed to hard work. The poses affected in many heroic Grecian statues suggest that the ancient Greeks were builders whose muscular bodies were shaped through hard manual labor, which was carried on daily.

If bodybuilding began as a result of the lifestyle of the ancient Greeks, then surely weight resistance training began with the Roman gladiators. These slave-warriors were forced to wield painfully heavy weapons—swords, shields, tridents, maces . . . the whole business. Those who survived such combat, with equipment that most likely weighed just a fraction less than their bodies, must have been formidable foes.

The Renaissance introduced the first paintings of muscular men, the works of my left-handed countrymen, Leonardo Da Vinci and Michelangelo. Their drawings and paintings differ in their interpretation of muscularity, and for good reason. Leonardo's passion for medicine actually motivated him to dissect cadavers and produce drawings from what he saw. Michelangelo left more to his imagination, and as a result, his paintings show more muscular size and less definition than do Da Vinci's drawings.

Competitive bodybuilding began in England. The earliest physique contests were little more than sideshow attractions at countryside fairs and carnivals. The contestants worked out with crude dumbbells fashioned from stones. England also produced the legendary Sandow, who introduced the entire "strongman" concept to America. Promoted by the fabulous Florenz Ziegfeld, Sandow blithely hoisted entire families and their children over his head. Three generations of relatives and their dogs from all over this country saw Sandow perform. His prowess generally reminded society that there actually was a masculine shape that one might have.

From the 1930s on, the sport spawned one or two significant heroes each decade. The 1930s introduced Charles Atlas (real name, Angelo Siciliano). Atlas could fairly be called one of the founding fathers of the bodybuilding business.

Stars of the 1940s included John Grimek, one of the all-time superstars of the sport and the man for whom the rule was passed forbidding Mr. America winners to succeed themselves. Grimek was probably further in front of the field of his day than any champion has been since. Toward the end of the decade, Steve Reeves rose to prominence. Grimek and Reeves won back-to-back Mr. Universe titles in London in 1949 and 1950. Reeves and many other excellent bodybuilders also appeared in a pleasant little musical film, *Athena,* in the early 1950s. (Of course, Reeves would grace the screens again, nearly a decade later, in a totally different role.)

Marvin Eder was another star of that era whose accomplishments especially intrigue me. He is widely considered one of the strongest bodybuilders who ever lived. Eder's records are still impressive today, but are truly dazzling by the standards of over thirty years ago: a 500-pound bench press (Eder weighed less than 200), 10 curls with 200 pounds, 10 *sets* of 10 chin-ups each with 200 pounds strapped to his waist. While there is no way to compare Eder's strength directly with mine, I can tell you that if we had had each other's motivation as training partners, we could have set strength records to stand until the next millennium.

The 1950s produced a flurry of bodybuilders who were heralded as the best of their time: Reg Park, one of Arnold Schwarzenegger's early idols; Clarence Ross; George Eifferman; and Bill Pearl. Pearl would go on to accomplish the astonishing feat of winning two Mr. Universe titles twenty years apart. And then the late '50s found bodybuilding receiving a great shot in the arm, in the form of Steve Reeves portraying Hercules in Italian movies. *Time* magazine called Reeves's acting "considerably more expressive than King Kong's," and *Life* magazine ran a feature on him. He was a box office sensation in Europe, where bodybuilding has always been extremely popular. And his films spawned many heroic imitators, including Mark Forrest ("Lou Degni" to the bodybuilding world), Ed Fury, Kirk Morris, Gordon Scott, and others. All their films missed cinematic greatness by a goodly margin, but they ushered in the 1960s and the rapid awakening of the country's consciousness toward fitness in general.

By the 1960s, bodybuilding contests were very popular. A Mr. Universe winner, Dave Draper, made films with Tony Curtis and Tuesday Weld. The two reigning stars of the decade were Larry Scott, who was the first Mr. Olympia, and Sergio Oliva, who held the title for the next three years after Larry Scott.

Sergio Oliva has the all-time classic bodybuilding physique. His body truly represents every bodybuilder's ideal—strength, muscularity, and definition.

After Sergio, the new bodybuilding stars were Arnold Schwarzenegger and Frank Zane. They were both Mr. Universe winners (each won several times). Arnold then went on to conquer the Mr. Olympia title seven times (six of those were won consecutively). I won the title after Arnold, and Frank Zane followed me as a Mr. Olympia winner. The first five Mr. Olympia winners—Scott, Oliva, Arnold, Frank Zane, and I—were all accorded superstar status. The movie and book *Pumping Iron* made the general public more aware of bodybuilders and bodybuilding.

Probably the most famous name in bodybuilding is the name *Weider*. For the past 40 years, Joe and Ben Weider have actively advanced the sport of bodybuilding. Ben Weider is the founder and president of the IFBB (International Federation of Bodybuilders). This is a worldwide association with tens of thousands of members. Joseph Weider is the founder of *Muscle & Fitness* magazine, which is one of the oldest and most popular bodybuilding publications around. He is an avid promoter of all aspects of health and fitness. Without the dedication of the Weider brothers, bodybuilding would not be where it is today.

There are all types of equipment manufactured today, ranging from free-style weights to specialized machinery for all parts of the body. Health clubs and gyms have a wide variety of equipment for all types of exercise, including training for other sports as well as bodybuilding. So the sport is truly advancing, with plenty of gyms, equipment, and new techniques and technologies.

Exercise is becoming more popular each day. Research has shown that physical exercise is the number one way to combat most degenerative diseases. The benefits are endless, and bodybuilding in particular is the greatest way to achieve a strong, healthy body. This book will advance your knowledge of bodybuilding and weight training so you can reap these benefits.

Franco Columbu's Complete Book of Bodybuilding

Chapter 1

A BASIC HEALTH & FITNESS PROGRAM

"Franco, you really make me feel ashamed of myself," a well-known television talk show host said to me recently after we had finished taping an interview. "I really wish I could stay in great shape the way you do, but I just don't have the time to get to the gym every day." He patted himself on the tummy and gave me an embarrassed smile. "But I'm afraid it's beginning to show."

That conversation really got me thinking. There are a lot of men in the same boat; so busy, they are reluctant to take time to exercise and take care of themselves. Also, many of them eat out very often and have difficulty in getting proper nutrition. But this reluctance about nutrition and exercise has unfortunate results. Many successful men let their health suffer and suddenly find their careers cut short by diseases associated with physical deterioration; a heart attack, stroke, or serious ulcer is simply too high a price to pay for success.

Health is too important an element of life to let slide. With a minimum amount of training and by watching your diet, you can protect your health as well as raise your energy level and your mental outlook. You will look better, feel better, and be a lot better at whatever you choose to do.

Exercise and nutrition are as much tools of business as the typewriter, the telephone, or factories. Without your health, nothing else can be achieved. But since finding time is a problem, I believe an important fitness program would be one that uses the absolute minimum amount of exercise (and, therefore, time) to protect against physical deterioration.

Maybe you cannot get to the gym regularly, or you spend a lot of time on the road and have trouble getting any amount of exercise. Nonetheless, by setting aside no more than 15-20 minutes a few times a week, you can put your body through enough training so that your health will not suffer. This kind of program will not get you in shape for the Super Bowl, but it will help to ensure that you are around for a great many football games to come.

The key to success lies in adapting your training to your surroundings. At home you can use some simple and basic equipment to aid you in your workouts. On the road you can substitute exercises that do not require the use of weights or other equipment. And no matter where you are, you can ensure that your muscles, tendons, joints, and ligaments are kept stretched and flexible, and that your abdominal muscles remain flat, hard, and strong.

Introduction to the Training Program

I have developed a training program for the busy person or executive so he or she can get the best workout in the shortest possible time. It also can be adapted for the person who travels a lot. The program works on the following three levels:

Warm-up and Conditioning Exercises—stretching movements and exercises to condition the abdominal muscles.

Beginning Resistance Exercises—using gravity and the weight of your own body to strengthen and develop your muscles and cardiovascular system.

Weight Training Exercises—accelerating the adaption of your muscles to exercise by the use of dumbbells.

This program is progressive. You begin with the first level, learn the exercises, and continue to do them until you feel you are ready to undertake more strenuous training. At that point, you add the second level to your training, but you don't abandon the first. Your workouts will now consist of both level one and level two, one level right after the other.

The second level of exercises will continue to strengthen your muscles and prepare you for the weight-training movements in the third level. The only equipment needed for this level of training is a pair of dumbbells. When you feel ready for level three, weight training, the level two exercises serve as a good preliminary warm-up.

There will be times when you don't have access to dumbbells or other weight-training equipment. When such times arise, you can rely on your second level exercises and merely do twice as many sets as you would if you were going to do level three exercises in your workout.

How Often to Train. I recommend that you try to exercise a minimum of three and a maximum of five days a week. You should try to schedule one day of rest between training days to give your body a chance to rest and recuperate.

When to Train. Some people prefer exercising in the morning when they are fresh, while others would rather train at the end of a busy day to help them relax and wind down from work. Either way is all right. Just avoid training too quickly after a meal, because this takes blood away from the stomach where it is needed for digestion.

Missing Workouts. Nobody is perfect, and you are bound to miss some scheduled workouts. If you do, simply go ahead and do your training at the next opportunity—later that day, in the evening, or even the next day. Don't feel too guilty if you miss some training, but be honest with yourself and realize that you will not get the benefits of health and strength you are seeking if you miss workouts too often.

Abdominals (Abs) and Stretching. The exercises in level one are unique in that you can do them more often than those in the other levels without interfering with the body's recuperation. Therefore I recommend that you do some stretching and ab work every day that you can. These exercises are especially important when you are traveling, since being on the road creates tension and tension can drain the body of energy.

About Equipment. Progressive resistance weight training works best when you add weight to an exercise whenever you find that movement is getting too easy. Therefore, a set of solid dumbbells that suits you one month, will be too light the next. If you never plan to become a bodybuilder, you should probably buy a pair of adjustable dumbbells to which you can add weight as you progress.

Level 1: Warm-up and Conditioning Exercises

Stretching movements are designed to elongate the muscle-tendon, joint-ligament structures of the body and to promote relaxation and the easing of tension. But it doesn't make any sense to do relaxing movements in a tense, aggressive manner. Take your time, use the breath to help relax the body, and give it time to stretch out.

Also, don't "bounce" in order to try and stretch the body a little further than it wants to go. This kind of movement actually sets off a reflex which causes the muscles to contract, and defeats your purpose.

#1 Hamstring Stretches. Stand on one leg and raise the other placing your heel on a table, chair, or some other object at hip height. Keep both legs straight. Then, raise both hands overhead and bend forward to touch your toes, ankle, or as far down the leg as you can reach. Hold this position for a moment, feeling the stretch in the back of the leg. Keep your back as straight as possible to promote stretching in the lower back as well as the hamstrings. Come up slowly into the starting position, then bend slowly forward and do another repetition. Keep the movement deliberate and fully under control.

Do 10 repetitions, then switch and do 10 more with the opposite leg.

#2 Standing Side Bends. Stand with your feet wide apart, hands on hips. Bend slowly to one side as far as you can. Hold this position a moment, then come back up to the starting position, and bend slowly as far as you can to the other side. Do not force the movement, but try to relax into it and stretch just a little more with each repetition.

Do 10 bends to each side.

Hamstring stretch.

Standing side bend.

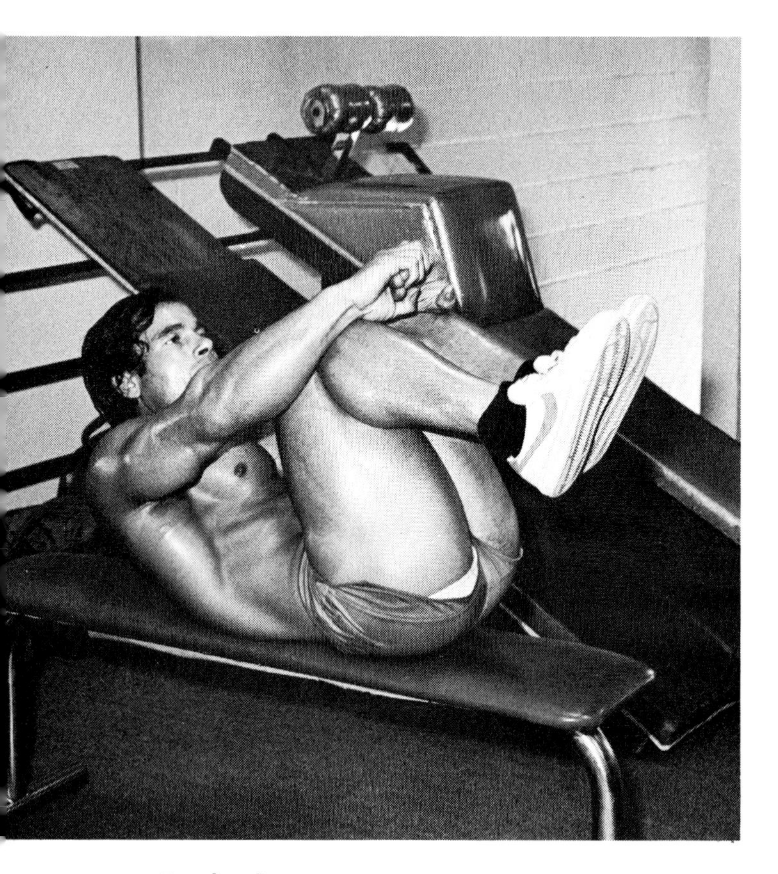

Bent-leg sit-up.

Bent-leg raise.

#3 Bent-Leg Sit-ups. (I recommend this variation of sit-ups because it takes all the strain off the lower back and still gives the abdominals a good workout.) Lie on your back—feet slightly off the floor and hands stretched out above you. Bend your knees and pull them as far up toward your chest as you can, simultaneously lifting your head and shoulders off the ground and bringing them up toward the knees. This movement feels difficult at first, but you soon will get used to it.

Do 3 sets of 15 repetitions each.

#4 Bent-Leg Raises. Lie on your back—hands under your buttocks for support and head slightly raised off the floor. Raise your legs as high as you can, bending your knees to keep the strain off your lower back. In this movement, the more you bend your knees, the easier the exercise.

Do 3 sets of 15 repetitions each.

#5 Lying Side Leg Raises. Lie on one side, supported by your elbow. Keep your upper leg straight and bend the lower one slightly for balance. Lift the upper leg as high as you can, then lower it slowly again, but do not let it touch the floor. Do a set with one leg, then turn over and do a set for the other.

Do 3 sets of 20 repetitions for each leg.

Lying side leg raise.

Level 2: Beginning Resistance Exercises

The only way to build strength and to shape and develop the muscles of the body is with resistance exercises. In this part of the program you will be working against the resistance of your own body's weight. This is convenient, since you will need no special equipment and can do these exercises anywhere.

Another kind of resistance you will need to encounter in exercising is the resistance of your cardiovascular system when called on to supply additional amounts of oxygen to working muscles. Therefore, I have included a very good aerobic exercise to condition the heart and lungs.

#1 *Push-ups.* Push-ups are still among the best exercises for strengthening the muscles of the chest, triceps (back of the arm), and deltoids (shoulders). Lie flat on your stomach—toes curled under and palms flat on the floor about even with your shoulders. Push up with your arms as far as you can, and lock out the elbows. Keep your back straight. This upright position is the starting position. From there, lower yourself so that your chest (but not your knees) just touches the floor, then push back up and lock out your elbows at the top. Continue to keep your back straight throughout the movement.

Incidentally, there is a good variation of this exercise for those who find it too difficult in the beginning, or who have difficulty getting through their sets doing the movement in a strict manner. In the variation, keep your knees on the floor as you do your push-ups. This gives you much less weight to lift and makes the exercise a lot easier.

At first, try to do as many traditional push-ups as you can. When you get too tired to do any more, switch over to the variation and finish your sets.

Do 3 sets of 10 repetitions.

Push-up.

Lunge using dumbbells for extra resistance.

#2 Lunges. Stand upright—feet together and hands on your hips. Keeping your head up and back straight, step forward with one leg, bend the knee, and lower yourself until the knee of your trailing leg just brushes the floor. Push back up, straighten your legs, and return to the starting position. Repeat the movement with your other leg.

Do 3 sets of 10 repetitions with each leg.

#3 Forward Bends. Stand with your feet comfortably apart and arms stretched straight overhead. Bend forward from the waist, keeping your arms above your ears to work the upper back. Continue forward as far as you can, feeling the stretch in the back of the legs. Hold for a moment, then raise back up, making sure the arms are stretched out and remain above the ears.

At the top of the movement, arch your back slightly and bend backwards to get the fullest range of motion. Throughout this exercise, keep your movements slow and deliberate to fully work the muscles of the lower back.

Do 3 sets of 20 repetitions.

Forward bend.

Between door press.

#4 Between Door Presses. Place your hands on either side of a doorframe at about shoulder height. Straighten your arms, then walk your feet back as far as possible. Make certain that your feet are not resting on a loose rug or some other slippery surface. From this starting position, bend your arms and let your body drop forward and through the door, with your feet remaining in place. From this extreme position, push yourself back to the starting position, straighten your arms, and lock out your elbows.

Do 3 sets of 10 repetitions.

#5 Running in Place. Stand upright and begin running in place, landing lightly on your toes. Once you feel warmed up, continue running, but now lift your knees as high in front of you as you can. Keep lifting the knees higher and higher. This type of running in place is best done like wind sprints, with short bursts of high-intensity effort, rather than long-term, low-intensity movement. Therefore, don't pace yourself. Go as hard as you can, as long as you can, then stop and take a short rest before trying another "sprint."

Do as much as you can of this exercise, and try to increase your efforts from workout session to workout session. Remember, your heart is a muscle, too, and it needs exercise just like the rest of the body. (Caution: Obviously anyone with heart problems, high blood pressure, or any other medical condition, should consult his or her own doctor before undertaking this or any other form of exercise.)

Running in place.

Level 3: Weight-Training Exercises

Muscles adapt to being used. And one way to speed up and optimize this adaptation is to add resistance to exercise movements. This is where weight training comes in. When you lift a weight, you are increasing the effect of gravity on the body, and making the muscles respond in super-normal ways. This extra resistance makes your muscles stronger and more healthy, and changes their appearance—giving them a firmer, more shapely look.

In all of the following movements, be deliberate and keep the weights under control. Don't throw them around and create all kinds of inertial forces that have nothing to do with making the muscle contract against resistance.

#1 Seated Dumbbell Curls. Sit on the edge of a bench or chair with a dumbbell in each hand hanging straight down at your sides. The palms of your hands should be facing one another. Keeping your back straight, "curl" the dumbbells upward, keeping your elbows unmoving and twisting your hands so that your palms face upward. Continue to lift the weights until they come as close to your shoulders as possible. Then, lower the dumbbells once more through the same wide arc—still not letting the elbows drift back—until they return to the starting position. Repeat the movement with the other arm. The twisting motion, or pronation and supination, of the wrists is done to minimize stress on the elbows.

Do 3 sets of 10 repetitions. You may alternate arms, which allows more concentration and intensity for each arm.

#2 One-Arm Rowing. Stand with feet apart, left foot forward, right foot back. Bend forward until your torso is parallel to the floor and rest your left hand on a chair, table, or other support for balance.

Take a dumbbell in your right hand and let it hang straight down from the shoulder. To begin the exercise, lift the weight straight up toward the shoulder, making sure you do not raise up to help the lift with your lower back.

Bring the dumbbell as close to the shoulder as possible, then lower it under control back to arm's length.

Do 3 sets of 10 repetitions with each arm.

Seated dumbbell curl.

One-arm rowing.

Triceps extension.

#3 Triceps Extensions. (This is a great exercise for the back of the arm, but a lot of people don't do it strictly enough to really get the full benefit.) Sit or stand upright and hold a dumbbell in one hand straight overhead. Keeping your elbow as close to your head as possible, lower the weight down behind your head as far as you can. It is important to keep that elbow tucked in and steady, or else you will end up working the shoulders instead of the triceps. Feel the stretch in the back of the arm, then lift the dumbbell up and back to the starting position, fully extended overhead.

Do 3 sets of 10 repetitions with each arm.

#4 Squats. (This is one of the best exercises for overall body development, especially for the thighs, as well as for the muscles of the abdomen and lower back.) Stand with your feet shoulder width apart. Take a dumbbell in each hand and let them hang at arms' length beside you. Keeping your head up, back straight, and feet flat on the floor, bend your

Squat.

knees and lower yourself until your thighs are parallel to the floor. Raise back up, straighten your legs, and return to the starting position.

A lot of people have difficulty keeping their feet flat on the floor during this movement. It is important not to come up on your toes, so place a board under your heels to help keep your balance.

Do 3 sets of 10 repetitions.

#5 Lateral Raises. (This is a combination movement designed to bring out the full shape and width of the shoulders.) Stand with your feet about 12 inches apart, a dumbbell in each hand. Bring the dumbbells together in front of you, palms facing one another. Lift the dumbbells straight out to the side and up, feeling the deltoid muscles working. Keep the elbows slightly bent to relieve strain, and raise the dumbbells to about level with the top of your head. As you raise the dumbbells, turn your wrists slightly so that palms face downward. This keeps the deltoids working instead of letting the biceps take over.

Do 3 sets of 10 repetitions.

Lateral raise.

Bent-over lateral raise.

Bent-Over Lateral Raises. Now for the second part of the combination—bend over so that your torso is nearly parallel to the floor and let the dumbbells hang straight down in front of you. Staying bent over, lift the weights out and up to each side and feel the back muscles squeeze together. Lift as high as you can, then lower the weights under control back to the starting position. These bent-over lateral raises will work the back of the deltoids as opposed to the front and sides.

Do 3 sets of 10 repetitions.

A Primer on Nutrition

Proper diet consists of a combination of a little special knowledge and a lot of common sense. Let me give an example:

Special knowledge—"The body requires a minimum of 60–80 grams of carbohydrate per day, and about 1 gram of protein for every 2.2 pounds of body weight."

Common sense—"If you feel you are too fat and you want to lose weight, you should eat less and exercise more."

When we talk about nutrition, we are, of course, concerned with food. Food provides us with energy and the nutrients we need to build and maintain tissue and sustain our various life processes. There are six basic nutrients in food:

1. *Protein*—the material of which our muscle structure is primarily constructed.
2. *Carbohydrate*—the material which provides us with ready energy in the form of glucose (sugar) in the body, and which fuels the activities of the brain.
3. *Fat*—the most efficient form of energy storage.
4. *Vitamins*—organic nutrients necessary for life processes.
5. *Minerals*—inorganic nutrients found both in our bodies and the planet on which we live.
6. *Water*—the most abundant substance in our bodies which assists in dissolving other nutrients and transports them to vital organs.

The only other item of specialized knowledge you need is an understanding of *calories.* The calorie is a unit of measure used to describe the amount of energy found in the food you eat, and the amount of energy you expend through exercise.

A pound of pure fat contains roughly 3,500 calories. This is equivalent to running (or walking) 35 miles. A pound of pure protein, on the other hand, has only about 600 calories. You can readily see from this that you can eat more protein than fat without putting on a lot of weight.

But many foods that are high in protein are high in fat as well—for instance, beef, ham, lamb, and many other meats. Fish and fowl, on the other hand, have relatively little fat, and so contain fewer calories.

Given these items of specialized knowledge, what then does common sense tell us?

- Eat low-fat meat, fish, chicken, or milk, yogurt, and cheese in preference to high-fat sources of protein.
- Eat a sufficient variety of foods (meat, fish, vegetables, fruits, etc.) to obtain the necessary amounts of the six basic nutrients.
- In addition to fat, avoid other calorie-loaded foods.

This last rule simply means eat fruit for dessert instead of foods packed with processed sugar, which contains a lot of calories and has no nutritional value—or avoid putting rich sauces on your food, loading your bread and potatoes with butter, pouring on the sour cream, and soaking your salads with high-calorie dressings (oil, like butter or margarine, is 100 calories a tablespoon!).

Suggestions for Eating Out

Following these suggestions is fairly easy at home, but much more difficult if you constantly eat in restaurants while on the road. Since I travel a great deal, here are a few of the tricks that I use.

- When the waitress brings a big plate of bread, make her take it away. If it isn't on the table, you won't eat it.
- When possible, order your food broiled or baked instead of fried (which adds oil and calories to your meal), and avoid ordering dishes where breading is used.
- If a meal comes with a sauce, have it brought on the side. You will add less to your entrée than the kitchen will. Do the same with salad dressing.
- Limit your alcohol intake. Liquor is fattening and harmful for your liver. If you must have a beer with your meals, get used to light beer—but don't have twice as many just because some have half the calories.
- Don't get too hungry. If you're famished when you sit down to eat, you'll probably eat too much.
- Take your time. Rushing meals is bad for your digestion. If you haven't got much time, order something that can be prepared quickly and digested easily. Do not order a heavy meal.

Other Factors Affecting Weight Control

The Exercise Quotient. Exercise is often overlooked as a factor in weight control. After all, if you run or walk a mile every day it will take you more than a month to lose just one pound. However, that means a loss of more than ten pounds in a year, which is a significant amount of weight.

Calorie restriction for weight loss works best if there is a concurrent increase in exercise. Cut back by 100 calories—a pat of butter, a shot of liquor—and then walk a mile. You will then lose weight at the rate of two pounds per month or more than 20 pounds per year. It takes so little to make such a big difference—if you just look at the long run.

Body Cycles. Remember that the body is

not a machine; it will not lose weight according to a rigorous schedule. It will even out in the long run, but the body takes its own time. So do not try weighing yourself every day, expecting to see uniform amounts of weight loss. Once a week is more like it.

You may have noticed that your body goes through cycles—some days you're up; some days you're down. This phenomenon is natural and by paying attention to your body's cycles, you can train, work, play, or do anything more effectively. That is, when your cycle is on an upward swing, you can train or work harder and benefit more from any activity. When you're down . . . do what I often do (when I'm on a down cycle): *take the day off.* Believe me, you'll be better off going with the natural flow of your body.

Weight Control vs Diet. Weight-loss diets are extreme variations of eating behavior that rarely produce permanent weight loss. What will help you to lose weight is to learn new eating habits, stick to them, and get the right amount of exercise. If you do this, your weight will take care of itself. Just remember, it has most likely taken you years or even decades to become overweight, so don't expect your body to reach a new equilibrium overnight.

Weight Gain. Some people feel they are too thin and want to gain weight. In that case, I recommend eating more calories in a balanced diet—a fourth meal each day, for example; and exercising as heavily as possible to build up an acceptable amount of muscle mass. The answer to thinness is not overeating to get fat. That is merely substituting one problem for another.

The Age Factor. After the age of 25 or 30, the body slows down at the rate of about ten calories per day per year. This means, if everything else remains the same, you will automatically gain a pound a year, which adds up to ten pounds in a decade. For this reason, even good eating habits need to be altered somewhat as we get older to reflect the changes in our metabolism.

A Final Word

Good looks, good diet, and good health all go together. Exercising and ensuring that your meals are balanced and nutritious are very important. But there is another aspect that, as a bodybuilder, I have been very conscious of. Bodybuilders work very hard to develop their physiques, but in a contest they also have to be concerned with *presentation.* A bodybuilder has to know how to show off what he's got.

The same is true for you. If you do not take care of your appearance, it is likely you are not taking care of business in other areas. Whether you are a bodybuilder or a businessperson, it is important to pay attention to keeping your skin clear and clean, knowing how to take care of overall grooming from your hair to your shoes, and choosing the kind of clothing that best represents who you are to the people you meet.

If you are to be at your best and be certain that those around you appreciate your good qualities, grooming, presentation, and creating the right impression are necessary adjuncts to maintaining health and good looks.

Chapter 2

GETTING STARTED ON THE BODYBUILDING LIFESTYLE

Training with weights as done by experts can be almost as individualized as bodies themselves. Naturally, the options increase as your abilities increase. The more advanced you become—that is, the more you know about your build and how your routines affect it—the more you can make efficient adjustments to your training program.

The secret of a successful beginner's routine is really to be on the right track from the beginning, and to be well-informed. Therefore, this chapter will cover what you need to know about weight training equipment, anatomy and how to apply your knowledge of anatomy to bodybuilding, training partners, and the proper attitude for bodybuilding.

Weight Resistance Equipment

Equipping yourself for training is not merely getting something for you to lift. You must *understand* how and why a piece of equipment fits into your training routine. Bodybuilding involves more brain muscles than you might imagine, and knowledge of equipment will enhance both your attitude and your workouts. (It's quite impossible to overestimate how important attitude is in bodybuilding.)

Your fundamental equipment should include a pair of dumbbells with fixed weights rather than adjustable ones; a barbell that can be adjusted to hold, say, 100 pounds (lbs.) to start; and a good solid bench that will remain stationary and not break. With this modest amount of equipment you can accomplish almost every major body movement practiced in bodybuilding, even those practiced by the champions.

Fixed dumbbells are preferable to adjustable ones, *especially for beginners,* because resetting the weight and retightening the collars between sets is a time-consuming process.

Fixed dumbbells are preferable to adjustable ones.

The muscle or muscle group being exercised will cool off partially during that time and the blood you've worked so hard to pump into that muscle will partially drain off. Both of these phenomena will defeat the purpose of your workout. Working out with minimum time between sets will not only bring optimum results, but is more beneficial to the cardiovascular system. Start with a pair of 25-lb. dumbbells; that is ample for all beginners' exercises recommended in this book. As you become more advanced, increase your equipment (by gradations of 5-10 lbs.) to include dumbbells up to 60 lbs.

As you add equipment to your training, you should consider other forms of barbells. A curling bar is essential for advanced arm development; this is a bar with ridges built into it so the hands can grip it at a 45-degree angle. This grip feels more natural at heavier weights, and also puts less strain on the elbows. Another good bar to have for rowing exercises is the T-bar, which permits the loading of weight at one end of the bar. Various supplemental benches well worth considering include the incline bench—very helpful in chest exercises and curls for the biceps—and the so-called Preacher's Bench, which makes possible a very strict and demanding curling exercise. And you may wish to consider cables, too; I believe cable exercises are very good for you.

A chinning bar would be a very valuable acquisition for advanced back exercises, but it is important that your chinning bar afford a wide grip. (The type that fits into a doorway is better than nothing, to be sure, but still will not stretch your back muscles enough for the best possible results.) A squat rack would also be a good idea; it is the best way for you to remove the weight from your back when you are finished with squatting exercises.

Shop around; avoid the bargains such as adjustable sets because once the clamps fail, you'll be buying another set. You will have a more efficient gym, and one that will pay you back many times over. Keep in mind that you are investing, not in equipment, but in your own physical improvement. If you want to live longer, buy equipment that will last longer and make you eager to want to use it year after year.

For advanced back exercises, a chinning bar is an invaluable piece of equipment. Hanging from the bar after heavy press exercises will decompress your spine. In addition, your bar should afford a variety of grips, especially wide grips as shown above.

Perhaps you would rather invest in a membership in a commercial gym. See if they have discounts for a five-year membership, but make certain the gym will be around that long. The success of a commercial gym depends on its location, the space you have available, and the investment you care to make. You must be certain that your gym offers something for everyone: the free-weight purists, the machine devotees, and the dabblers who are somewhere in between. The principal virtue of machines is that many athletes can train simultaneously, plus the safety factor; you can pick up a bench-press apparatus, for example, and if you don't like it you can let go without doing yourself the slightest harm.

To be sure, there are many advocates of various kinds of weight-resistance equipment. I have hardly touched the surface, nor do I intend to go any further. You can spend your valuable training time testing out all kinds of equipment or you can use it to train with just the few simple pieces I have mentioned. I think experimenting has its place in bodybuilding, but testing equipment can distract you from the main purpose of bodybuilding. What I have told you is all you need to know to get started.

Anatomy

To thoroughly benefit from weight training, you need to understand the mechanics of the body. The entire body works as a unit, one structure affecting another. As you probably remember from your high school science classes, the human body is developed from just a single cell. All cells spring from that single cell, subdividing over and over again, millions and millions of times as the body develops.

Muscle cells grow and subdivide pretty much as other body cells do. They must have exercise, of course; but they depend solely on organic compounds—carbohydrates, lipids, and protein—for nourishment. We will take a closer look at this in the Nutrition chapter.

What I would like to discuss is the relation of bodybuilding and the various specialized cell groups of the body. Each part of the body requires special attention by anyone, but especially by the bodybuilder. So, in no particular order, let's examine these parts.

Skin

The largest organ in the body is the skin. An average adult male has nearly 3,200 square inches of surface-area skin; and if it could be detached from its wearer, that skin would weigh almost 7 pounds—twice as much as the brain or the heart. The skin receives close to one-third of all circulated blood. Human skin is about as perfect a job of waterproofing as you are ever likely to see. Yet as important as it is to good health and fitness, skin is generally overlooked in bodybuilding. Good skin tone enhances good muscle tone (and, naturally, thick skin detracts from muscularity). Roller coaster weight changes—bulking up and then cutting down—can cause stretch marks if the fluctuations in weight are too extreme. Proper care of your skin starts from the inside out by eating a balanced diet. No creams or special preparations will do as much for your skin as good eating.

Bones

Under the epidermis and dermis (the outside and inside layers of skin) is the supportive structure of the body, the skeletal system. The 206 bones that make up the human skeleton enable a person to stand erect and accomplish body movements. Bones protect organs, and manufacture nourishing blood cells from bone marrow. And they provice *storage* for salt and various minerals, such as calcium, phosphorus, manganese, and magnesium to name a few. The more minerals a bone has, the stronger it is. Thus, mineral deficiencies invite injuries.

For example, 99 percent of your body's calcium is stored in your bones. Calcium is particularly important in bodybuilding because it is required for muscle movement, especially the ability to relax muscles in between contractions. Because calcium helps you relax generally as well as intramuscularly, a lack of it can leave you highly irritable. A calcium deficiency can also cause weak heart muscles, and can interfere with the process of blood coagulation. A good, healthy calcium (and magnesium) count has been known to make a difference of up to two weeks during the first twelve weeks of healing a broken bone.

Nature has preordained a correct position for your bones to be in to afford optimum blood circulation, nerve supply, and muscular strength. All of these capacities are obviously critical to bodybuilding because exercise provides mechanical stress for bones. Stress, particularly in weight bearing, triggers bone growth. Another little understood spur to bone formation is the effect of muscles contracting and pulling against their bony attachments. Remember, the anatomical function of a muscle is to connect two bones together; if a bone is out of place, its muscle will lack leverage and be weaker. Weaker muscles can also result from misaligned bones which pinch nerves. In either case, you can become prone to pain, injury, or both.

Joints

One area of anatomy in which we can get a good look at the advantages of using free weight is the joints. Body joints simply must have free movement. Joints are relatively vulnerable to abuse and they have wicked ways of getting even with their abusers. For instance, arthritis (as you probably know) is nothing more than an inflammation of a joint caused by too much wear and tear. Furthermore, damaged knees have ended a chilling number of athletic careers.

Knees. Knees are worth a special look, since they are at once the most important bodybuilding joints and the most poorly constructed joints in the body, given the loads and torques they are called upon to handle. In all forms of weightlifting, the knee carries the greatest stress. (Remember that the knee has plenty to do merely in walking, and getting you up and down stairs, in and out of chairs and cars, and so forth.) *The knee was only designed to bend forward.* So if you execute a squatting movement with your feet either splayed or pigeon-toed, you are only inviting disaster. (The correct squat is done with the feet about 12 inches apart and pointing straight forward, and in a forward movement, to afford the knee minimal stress.)

Shoulders. Unlike the other joints in the body, which are supported by ligaments, the shoulder joint is mainly supported by muscles. Because of this muscular support, the shoulder can move in a variety of directions. That is why it's important to build up and train the shoulders from all angles. An imbalance in training the shoulder muscles will hamper your use of this versatile joint; all the muscles must support the shoulder joint equally.

Elbows. The elbow joint is like the knee joint. It was designed to move one way, like a hinge. Ligaments hold this joint together, muscles contract and relax to make it move. These muscles require balanced training—this means that the triceps muscles, which extend the elbow joint, need more work than the biceps, which flex the elbow joint. You must be careful not to restrict the movement of the elbow, for example, in using a curling machine. The machine may not move in the same direction your elbow wants to and you can damage the elbow that way.

Ankles and wrists. Both of these joints are similar in that they have many small bones held together by ligaments and put into motion by muscles. The forearm muscles must be trained so the wrist can move in all directions. The calves are involved in ankle movements of various kinds. Again, the muscles attached to these joints must be stretched sufficiently to avoid injury, built up to provide strength, and trained to add gracefulness to their movement.

Muscles

As for the muscular system itself—without which there would obviously be no bodybuilding at all—the human body actually houses *three* kinds of muscles: striated, cardiac, and smooth. The latter include internal organ muscles, which work and contract involuntarily (by themselves), the cardiac muscles, which work the same way to pump the heart, and the striated muscles, which are those we control directly. Muscles (of all types) comprise 50 percent of body weight, and muscle contractions affect all body movement, help the diaphragm, and aid in blood circulation, digestion, and lymph flow.

All muscle movement is the responsibility of the motor unit of the nervous system. A

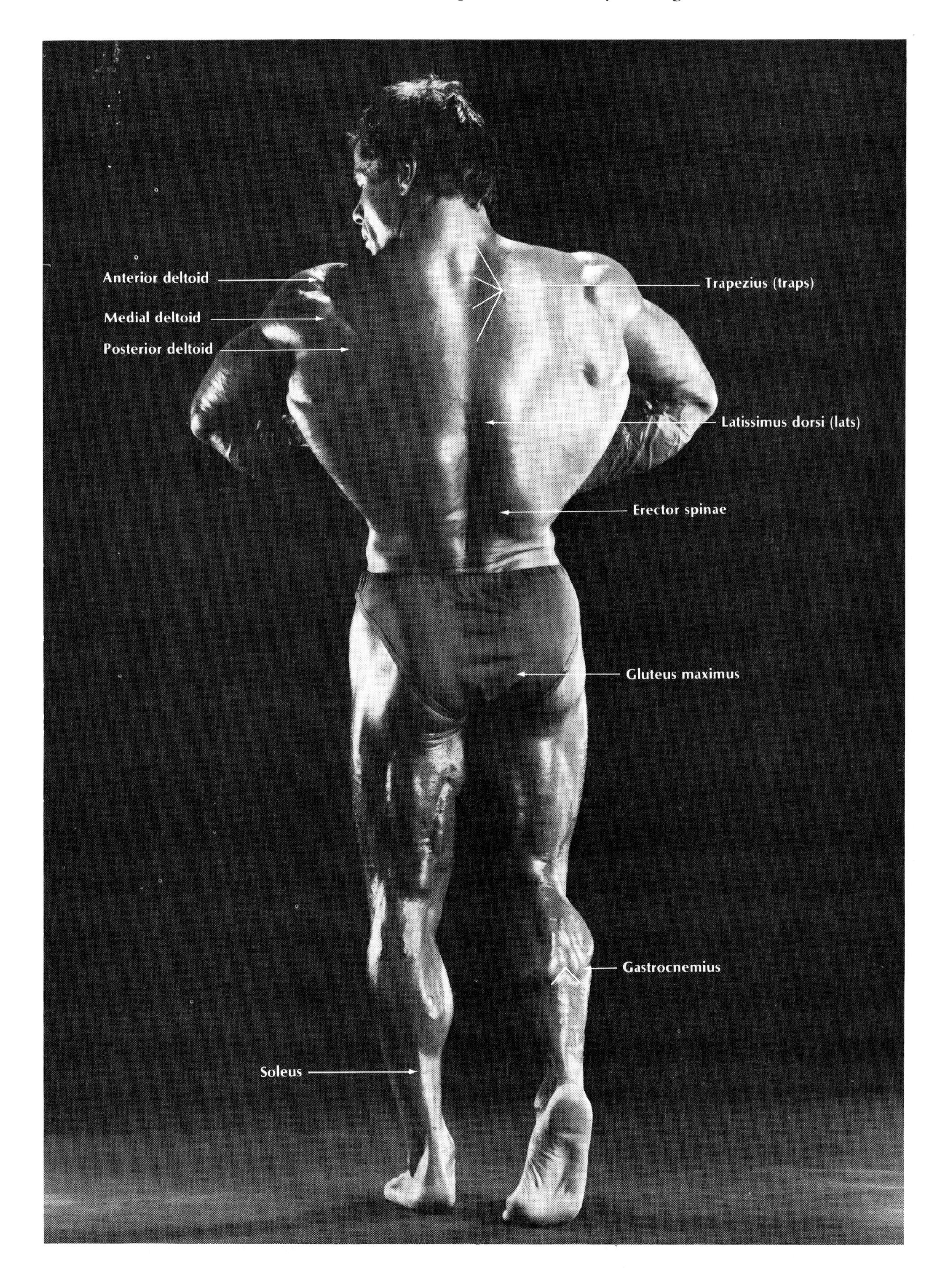
Anterior deltoid
Medial deltoid
Posterior deltoid
Trapezius (traps)
Latissimus dorsi (lats)
Erector spinae
Gluteus maximus
Gastrocnemius
Soleus

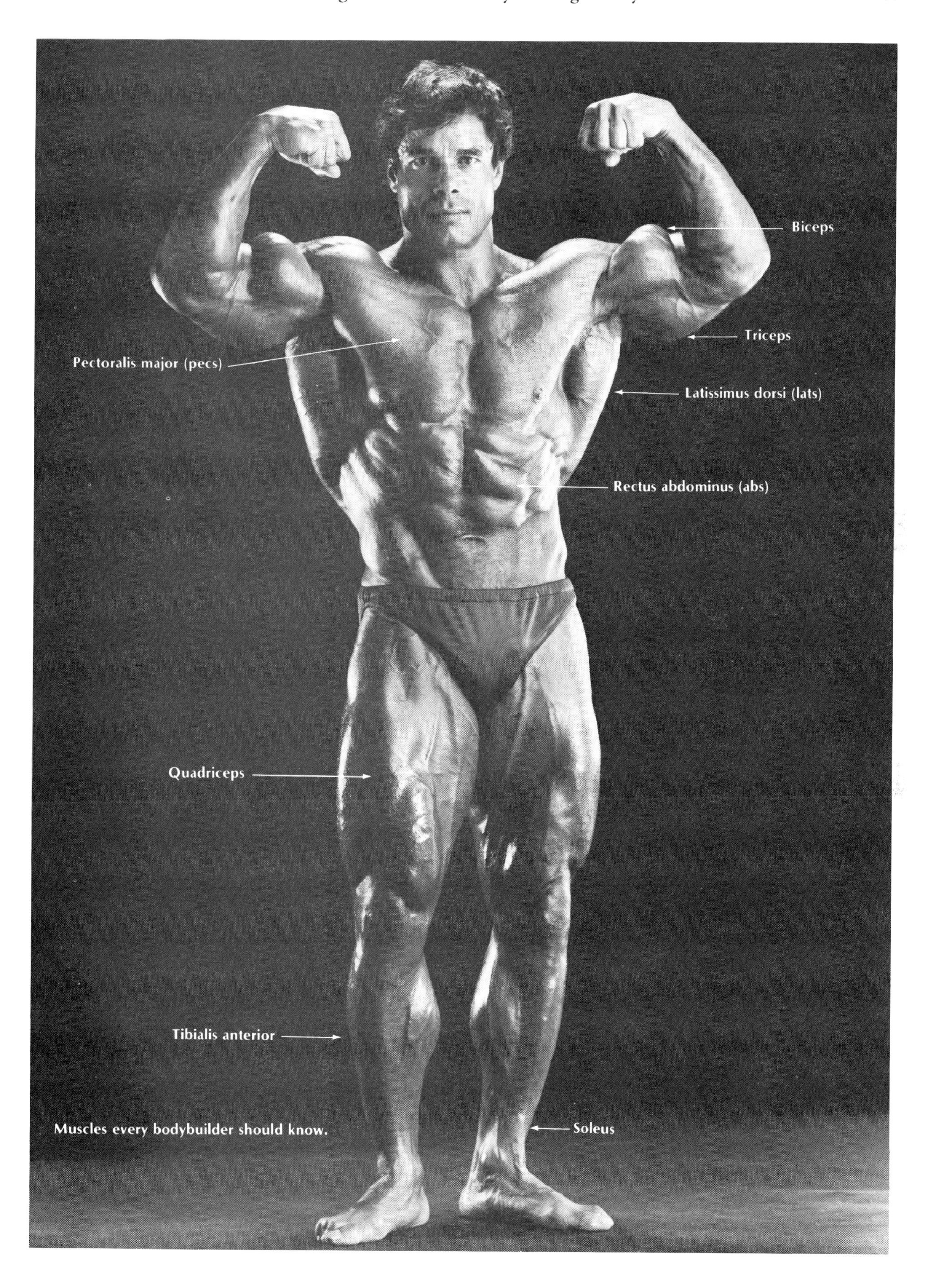

Muscles every bodybuilder should know.

muscle will weaken immediately with the loss of as little as 1 percent of its nerve supply. The strength of any muscle contraction is determined by the total number of motor units contracting, and the number of times per second the motor unit is stimulated. (A muscle contraction must last .1 second or more to be a true contraction.)

When a muscle or group of muscles that we normally control through movements, contracts *in*voluntarily, that is called a muscle *spasm.* It occurs when the nerve motor is sending too many impulses to the muscle to allow it to relax (such as in the case of cramps). A most common cause, as we have noticed in our practice, is calcium or magnesium deficiency.

Good muscle tone is *not* exclusively a product of good training. Muscle tone depends as well on a continuous flow of stimuli from the spinal cord to the nerve motors. What training can accomplish is to help the nervous system and the muscles both work together and work better.

More factors than you might think are anatomically involved in a muscle's contracting and relaxing. The nervous system, calcium, and *enzymes* all enhance contractions. (Enzymes are large protein molecules that make use of what we eat. They act like a catalyst does in organic chemistry, speeding the rate of intercellular reaction.)

Specifically, the nerve endings or *synapses* produce a substance called *acetylcholine.* This substance goes into the muscular area, and stimulates and causes the contraction. No acetylcholine, no contraction. In order to *relax* the muscle, a second substance, *acetylcholine stelase,* breaks down the acetylcholine so the muscle fibers can relax and become stimulated again with acetylcholine.

Regarding muscle contraction and relaxation from a training point of view, keep in mind that nature designed your muscles to contract, not to relax, and they should be trained in accordance with what nature had in mind. For that reason, I find it undesirable to emphasize the *negative* movements of training (that is, that portion of the movement which returns the weight to starting position). A muscle contraction takes .01 second (and must be maintained for 10 times that long), but muscle relaxation takes twice as long. And since you obviously can't contract and relax a muscle at the same time, the effort you put into forcing a negative movement is largely wasted.

You cannot train your smooth (involuntary) muscles directly, but good muscle tone outside invariably indicates better tone in the smooth muscles, too. For instance, consider the cardiac muscle, which contracts by itself and allows the coronary artery—the hardest-working part of the body—to feed the heart. A normal heart beats 72 times a minute, which is 4,320 times an hour; 103,690 times a day; and so on, up to billions of times in a lifetime. But the heart of an athlete—such as a bodybuilder—beats more slowly than that, perhaps as slowly as 50 times a minute. And that can parlay into an additional 20 or 25 years of life for the heart. It's not *automatic,* of course, that you'll live longer if you're an athlete; however, a strong, healthy heart keeps your other vital organs in better condition.

Central Nervous System

As long as we're talking about lifespan, let's consider your longest-lived aspect, the central nervous system (brain and spinal cord). It's the very first element of you to begin growing at your birth, and it will be the very last to die. The nervous system controls all movement and muscle contraction. Nerve cells link up lengthwise to send messages anywhere to the body from the brain. These messages take the form of impulses, which begin as an electrical charge from the brain but are somehow transformed into a *chemical* change by the time they reach a muscle.

The chemicals most important to your nervous system are potassium and sodium, because these minerals aid in the conduction of nerve impulses. This conductivity is necessary for muscle function and for enzyme distribution to aid in converting amino acids into the materials the body uses for repair and growth. An imbalance of sodium and potassium can affect nerve conductivity adversely to either extreme, too much or too little. It can also have an adverse effect on hormone production and glandular function. That is why, for example, using salt pills can be a grievous mistake for an athlete or for anybody.

We all know that you can have too much of a good thing, and salt pills deliver more sodium than nature wants your nervous system to have. Once the alarm goes out that there's too much sodium intruding, your body tries to wash it out with water, and you run a serious risk of dehydration. Many bodybuilders think that by eliminating fluid from the body, they will have more definition. Actually, they end up looking dry in the skin, which makes you look unhealthy and older than you really are. (This can attract the judge's attention and cause him to think you are ill.)

The human brain is the most complex organ of the body. It's actually made up of billions of nerve cells. And if you think computers are sophisticated, consider this: If you could build a computer of the tiniest microcircuitry, each circuit to correspond to a brain cell, and you wanted that computer to be the equivalent of a human brain, you would still need a space about *100 stories high* to house your computer!

Another nervous system, the *autonomic* nervous system, controls the smooth muscles, heart, and glands. The pituitary gland acts as a kind of First Sergeant among the glands; it produces a hormone that stimulates all the other glands. The pituitary gland feeds solely on carbohydrates and oxygen. That's why it's a mistake, even among bodybuilders, to sacrifice carbohydrates in favor of very high-protein diets. Carbohydrates are the source that supplies you energy for training. The food and oxygen contained in your blood are supplied to the brain by the carotid artery, and in the final analysis, healthy brain cells are more important than healthy muscle cells. Increase your protein intake if you want to, but be sure to include carbohydrates in your diet to stay healthy and strong.

Other important glands include the endocrine system of eight glands, which secrete hormones; the thyroid gland, which ultimately determines how fast you gain muscle definition, not to mention how it regulates your metabolism; the parathyroid, which controls calcium for your entire body; the pancreas; renal; pineal; and the ovaries (in women) and testes (in men).

There are 31 pairs of spinal nerves exiting the spinal cord through the vertebrae (8 pairs in the cervical spine, 12 in the thoracic area, 5 in the lumbar area, 5 in the sacrum, and one in the coccyx or tailbone). Joint and muscle problems are frequently caused by a malfunction of nerves supplying the injured area. In my practice of chiropractic care, I have found vertebral relationships to upper-body problems in 80–90 percent of the athletes I've treated. In these cases, naturally, I treat the injured area so the athlete gets relief from pain, but I work to free the *nerves* involved at the same time, which often speeds recovery. Let's look at one example of that, relating directly to bodybuilding.

Not long ago, I had a patient whom I also knew from the gym. He came to me not because he was in pain, but because he was *losing* size in his thighs despite some heavy squatting in his workout program. My examination showed some pinched nerves in his lumbar area (the lower back); bones were compressed, thus displaced—from all the squatting he had been doing—and were cutting off an appreciable amount of nerve supply. As I pointed out earlier, it doesn't take much of that kind of loss to weaken a muscle, and his loss of an inch in his thighs was dramatic proof of such weakening.

I made adjustments in the lumbar area—not the thighs—along with a recommendation that he cut back or eliminate his squats from his routine. He followed my advice and his thighs began to grow again—almost at once. Unfortunately, he took that to mean that everything was all right, resumed his heavy squatting, and was back in my office on weakened thighs in no time. After a few such stubborn cycles, I convinced him to give up squats altogether. Leg presses and thigh extensions then got the job done.

Circulatory System and the Heart

The circulatory system complements the nervous system, and is almost as important to the bodybuilder. Proper circulation brings enzymes, proteins, vitamins (which are really co-enzymes, and can only function beneficially if enzymes are around), defensive mechanisms, minerals, and oxygen to all body parts.

An average human has about six liters of blood, and the heart pumps that much every minute. That's why a sensible weight program will include some running or other high-repetition exercise for the cardiovascular system. Bodybuilding itself is of some cardiovascular benefit, especially if you train quickly with minimal rest between sets.

If you can lower your pulse from 72 (normal) to 50, you can save a billion heartbeats over your lifetime. And, if all else goes well, add up to 25 years to your life.

It is true that athletes develop larger hearts, but in and of itself that is quite all right. A bigger heart can pump more blood more efficiently than a smaller heart and therefore has more time to rest.

The oxygen content of your blood also is important to training. We normally breathe 16–18 times a minute, quite a bit fewer than the number of beats of the heart but it is still a sufficient rate. Man has about 3 liters' volume in his lungs; exertion will increase that another half-liter or so, and under force, the capacity can be almost *doubled*—in other words, your lungs can do a lot more than you think. So breathe deeply, increase the volume of your lungs and the amount of oxygen in your blood, and exhale hard to get rid of as much carbon dioxide as possible. The more oxygenated your blood, the better job it can do of nourishing your muscle tissues and helping them grow. You will discover just how enjoyable your "pump" can be.

Body Types

Finally, let's consider the three basic body types, and the basic differences in their fundamental approach to training. The types are *ectomorphic* (thin), *endomorphic* (heavy), and *mesomorphic* (muscular). Any one of the types can be a successful bodybuilder, and every mortal who ever drew breath has at least some—even if minimal—traits of all three types, no matter how dominant one type may seem to be.

Ectomorphs are naturally built along slight and linear proportions, with long muscles and, usually, long arms and legs. Gaining weight is a particular problem for ectomorphs and, of course, you simply cannot gain muscle size without gaining weight, too. So it makes sense for athletes of this body type to add extra protein to their diets without sacrificing natural carbohydrates. Their training routines should favor more sets with heavier weight, but fewer repetitions in general. Ectomorphic bodybuilders also must put in extra work on those long arms and legs to achieve proportion. And because their muscles are usually longer, ectomorphs must warm up more thoroughly with stretching exercises before training. The good news is that athletes of this body type can develop tremendous muscular definition with hard work.

Endomorphs are built along much thicker lines—thick arms, legs, muscles, even bones—and generally have a slow metabolism, which allows them to get fat more easily than the other types. Endomorphs' problems are pretty much the opposite of ectomorphs'. Diet is critical; intake of fats should be severely limited. Since muscular definition, or "cuts," represents the endomorphs' most difficult goal, their training routines should incorporate less sets with lighter weights and higher repetitions. They also should do a greater variety of exercises per body part, with an absolute minimum of rest between sets (no more than 60 seconds). These individuals should set out to reduce fat first, then build muscle. The endomorph who succeeds in disciplining himself through that sequence is well on his way to attaining contest stature, should he desire that. "Trim first, build second" is a marvelous concept for contest training even though many bodybuilders mistakenly believe the opposite.

Mesomorphs are built like me; that is, they have thick, rugged muscles and combine the best features of the other two body types. Mesomorphs, then, are the most naturally muscular body type. They generally tan well and enjoy good skin tone. Along with their healthy skeletal structure, they indeed have a head start on other beginners. These athletes should balance their diets with protein, fats, and carbohydrates, and train with heavy weight, medium repetitions.

Most of us are combinations of the different body types. It is important to be aware of what body type you have, but do not be overly concerned because each type or combination can achieve a champion goal.

Application of Anatomy to Training

Bodybuilding today is far more industrialized than it has ever been. We are now in "The Space Age of Bodybuilding," and it is moving ahead at rocket speed. Companies are working closely with research physiologists to develop equipment according to the mechanics of the human body. However, you will still have to analyze your own particular body type and structure to find out what machines work best for you. You should note how your muscles respond after training. Trained muscles should feel good and a good pump should also develop.

What is a pump? When you train a muscle, stimulation takes place which brings extra blood to that area. The extra blood gives the muscle the appearance of slight swelling and this is called a *pump.*

Speaking of the pump, one of the best tips I can give you is this: During training, try to *visualize* your muscle becoming pumped full of rich, oxygenated blood. Watch your muscles in the mirror as you exercise them; watch them directly when you can (such as during curls); or merely try to visualize the phenomenon without looking anywhere. The bodybuilder who masters visualizing his pump will enjoy measurably better results than the one who doesn't, even if they train with identical routines.

Always make sure that in every exercise you are working the muscle directly involved. There is more than one exercise for every body part so that the muscles will be worked from different angles. Some of the basic exercises are done better with free weights, but you can also use machines for each of the training programs in this book. All forms of weight training and bodybuilding depend upon the law of gravity, except the new hydraulic machines. The hydraulic system gives resistance from every directon.

The first step in applying your training to your own anatomy is to analyze your body type. Endomorphs, for instance, must anticipate routines with 3-5 more repetitions in every set; ectomorphs should plan on doing fewer reps but with more weight. And equally important, you should keep careful track of which of your muscles grow the easiest, and which ones grow the least. This is critical to your individual routine for two reasons:

- Sometimes the muscles that you decide are your slowest growers should be trained first. This gives you maximum energy at the start, and those stubborn muscles benefit from the first and best nutrition your blood has to give.
- Muscles which grow easily for you will very likely grow just as well no matter where in your routine you schedule them.

So, if you detect a muscle weakness (and virtually every bodybuilder does have that

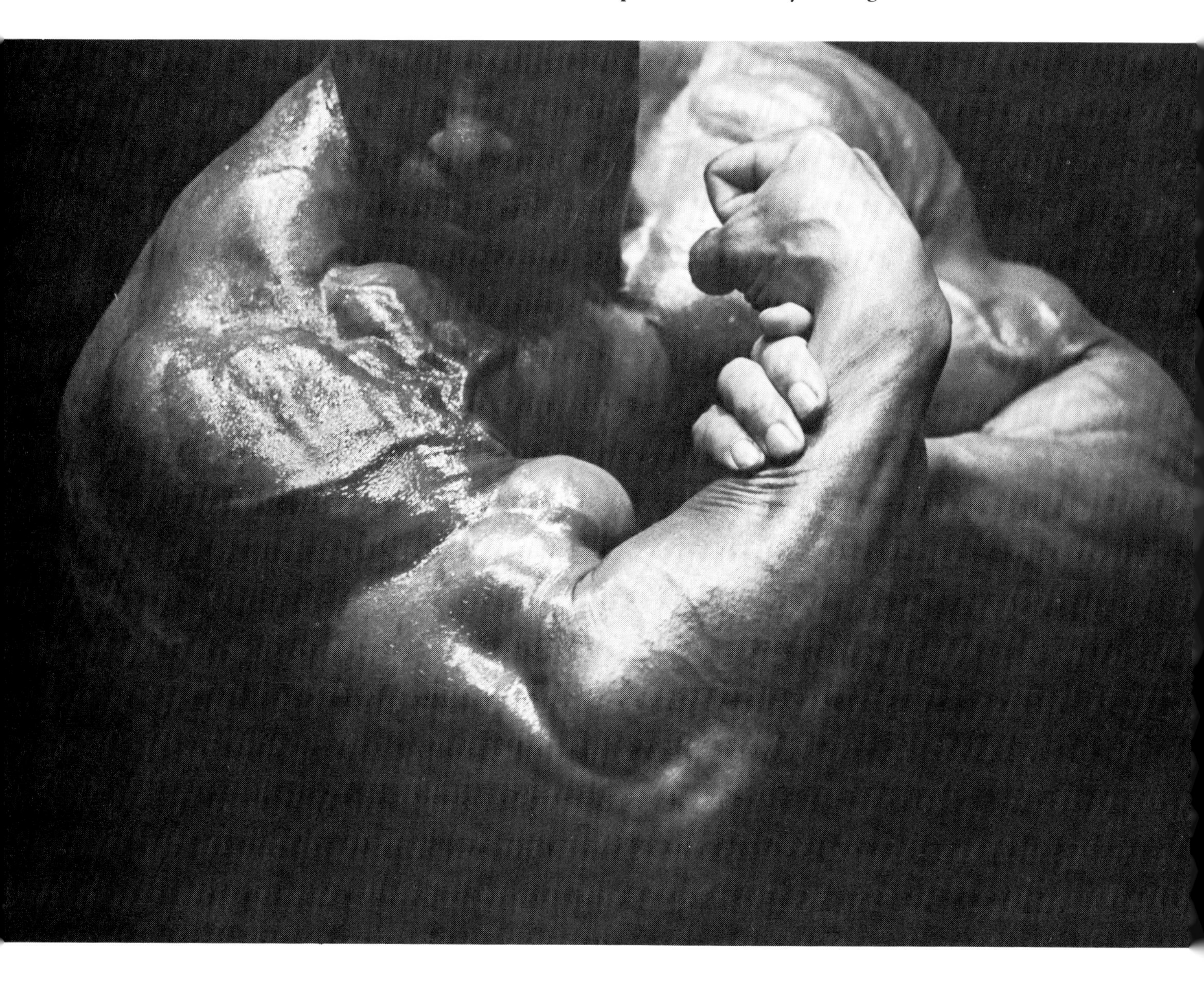

kind of imbalance to some degree), change your sequence from what will be suggested here. If your shoulders are coming along better than your arms, try working your arms first, even though the opposite would normally be recommended.

Anatomical individuality also makes it perfectly OK to *cheat* the exercise, within reason, using slightly more weight. You've just got to *feel out* any given exercise in that specific muscle to decide whether swinging the weight, as opposed to lifting it slowly and strictly, might be the boost you need.

Your first exercise for any body part should be the most effective and the one that permits the use of the most weight. Your second exercise should be your second most effective, and so on. Therefore you must learn which exercises work best for you. But in changing your routine, for the sake of variety and for keeping your point of view fresh, you should leave your first and second most efficient exercises as they are and make adjustments from the third exercise on down.

Number Ones—Exercises by Priority

I'm going to provide you with a table listing, in order of most-efficient exercises, exercises for every major muscle group. I have

NUMBER ONES

Chest
1—Bench press
2—Incline press
3—Dips*
4—Dumbbell flyes

*Keep your head up and your chest forward; otherwise the exercise will work your triceps more thoroughly than your chest.

Shoulders
1—Lateral raises*
2—Press behind neck
3—Front dumbbell raises
4—Upright rowing
5—Shrugs

*Equally effective: Bent-over lateral raises, which do a more thorough job on the posterior cap of the deltoid (remember your shoulders are actually comprised of *three* caps of muscles—front, side, and rear).

Triceps
1—French triceps extension, lying on back
2—Triceps pushdowns*
3—Sitting barbell triceps extensions
4—One-arm triceps extensions, or cable triceps extensions

*One of the rare apparatus moves that can't be duplicated any other way.

Biceps
1—Incline dumbbell curls
2—Sitting (or standing) dumbbell curls
3—Preacher's bench
4—Standing barbell curls
5—Concentration curls

Forearm (A very tough, stubborn muscle)
1—Standing forearm flexion extension*
2—Palms-up wrist curls on a bench
3—Reverse wrist curls

*This is an exercise I have pioneered. You simply hold the dumbbell by your side at arm's length, and rotate it as far as you can in each direction. Its advantage is that it also works the weaker forearm muscles that help you raise the *back* of the hand.

Back
1—Chins*
2—T-bar rowing
3—Barbell rowing
4—Machine pulldowns
5—One-arm rowing

*Best by far, whether you do them with the bar in front of your chin or behind your neck. Use a wide grip.

Thighs
1—Squat and leg presses
2—Leg extension*
3—Front squat
4—Leg curls**
5—Running

*The best single exercise for the front thigh (quadriceps).
**The best exercise for back thighs (thigh biceps, or, more popularly, the hamstrings).

Calves (Another tough muscle)
1—Donkey raises*
2—Standing calf raises with maximum weight
3—Sitting calf raises
4—Front calf raises

*This may be a surprise #1 choice. I recommend it because, when the body is bent forward, all the calf muscles are in a stretched position—giving maximum results.

Abdominals and Waist
1—Crunch-type or flat sit-ups*
2—Straight-leg raises
3—All other abdominal exercises—bent-leg raises, side leg raises, side bends, and so on—are of approximately equal value. Ideally, you should do a set of each in rotation, then go back and start again. I have an entirely new system for the abdomen that is more effective and quicker than any other I have found, which I'll discuss soon.

*The roman chair sit-up is known for abdominal work. However, it works the abdomen 20 percent of the time while the lower back is strained 80 percent of the time. I have worked with hundreds of bodybuilders who have had lower back pain, and found their iliopsias muscles in spasm due to using the roman chair. I do not recommend doing roman chair sit-ups for anyone.

determined this order after many years of experience in weight training and my chiropractic education. More bodybuilders have benefited from giving priority to certain exercises than from any other weight training technique. Still, you may find that lower-ranked exercises feel better and produce better for you than my recommendations. If that happens because of the individuality of your build, increase emphasis on those exercises.

I think you'll find that my list of Number Ones is far and away the best-working exercises you'll find.

Training Intervals

However your exercises are ultimately combined, you must remember that a basic bodybuilding principle is: *Today You Train, Tomorrow You Recuperate.* That's why beginners should train only three times a week—to get at least one day of rest in between workouts. That three-times-a-week schedule assumes that you're training your entire body those three times. Should you increase your schedule to *four* workouts a week, each body part should be trained only twice. Ideally, you'll give the exercised muscle groups *more* rest, because in a four-times-weekly routine, you should be doing more exercises per body part. For example, if you train your upper body on Monday and your lower body on Tuesday, then take Wednesday off completely. Repeat the sequence on Thursday and Friday. Take a close look at this schedule and you'll see that it actually allows each muscle group two days' rest in between workouts.

What is the correct order in which to train the various muscle groups? is one of the most commonly asked questions from beginners. The best answer is that it is not quite as important as most people think. I've probably tried every mathematical permutation of exercise combinations that exists. Some combinations were better than others, but other factors are much more significant, such as the order in which you do the specific exercises for any given muscle group and how correctly you do them.

In general, a good idea to help you create a body-parts sequence is that larger body parts (back and chest) are easier to train at the beginning of your workout than at the end, because they need more sets. As to what muscle group should follow, it's usually effective to train a muscle group that was receiving blood secondarily while you were exercising a muscle group close by. For instance, most exercises for the chest will help you achieve a partial pump in the shoulders, so they would be a good group to train next. Shoulder exercises will affect the triceps, so triceps exercises would be a logical next step; and so on.

You're not going to want to take the same routine into the gym forever and ever; you should switch your muscle-group sequence around every now and then, both to stay fresh mentally and to have a better chance of *shocking* the muscle groups. (Muscle growth slows down drastically if the muscle group becomes accustomed to the exercise you've planned for it. You've got to surprise your muscles periodically.)

The flexibility you have in choosing a body-parts sequence does *not* mean that you've got *carte blanche* when it comes to the sequence of the exercises themselves. It's extremely important for you to do the best exercises first for the various muscle groups as I prescribed in the previous section.

Needless to say, when an exercise actually *hurts* you (as opposed to merely making a muscle sore), you must find another way of accomplishing the same move. Pain means something is wrong and is only going to get worse if you do not make a change. Try to determine which exercise is the real cause of your pain, not merely which muscle hurts.

Here's another way to look at training intervals between workouts: Three times weekly is the ideal, should your objectives be both size and definition gains. If you train each body part *twice* weekly, your principal gains will be in size, not definition. *Once* a week will net you gains mostly in size. And if you train each body part *four* times weekly, you'll gain in definition, and less size.

A beginner whose fat content is high should train more often (and watch his or her diet). A beginner who comes to the sport thin (with a very low fat content) should increase the amount of weight he or she uses and train no more than two or three times per week. But the majority of beginners are somewhere in between.

Most, but not all, body parts respond very well to a regimen of being trained three times in one week and two times in the next. Calves and abdominals can be trained up to four or five times a week. But the arms—and this may surprise you—respond best to being trained twice a week. Your arms get a pretty fair workout doing all the other upper-body exercises, and since arm muscles are smaller to begin with, it's easy to overtrain them.

Now, let's take a closer look at a year's worth of training prior to a physique contest—not because you aspire to competitive bodybuilding but so you can see how the body responds to an ideal routine. If I had a year to get ready for, say, the Mr. Olympia contest, I would spend the first six months emphasizing my weak body parts and merely maintaining my stronger muscle groups. For the next three months or so, I would round out the routine so that the exercises would be better balanced between weak and strong parts. (I would maintain a well-balanced nutritional program with vitamin and mineral supplements.) And that would leave me roughly 100 days—the first 20 for complete rest and recuperation from minor injuries and mental staleness and the last 80 to blast ahead at maximum weight and full power. Within the first three weeks of those last 80 days, I would be at the absolute peak of training, doing as many sets of as many reps with as much weight as I could handle. Along with that, I would increase my protein intake, and take all the vitamins I thought I would need.

A point I would like to make here is that the last three months out of a year of training are the right time to supplement your exercise with increased nutrition. I have found it most beneficial to have a complete blood study done along with a hair mineral analysis at this time so that I could better balance my supplements (vitamins, minerals, and enzymes). These tests are available at most chiropractic centers and through most holistic practitioners.

You should not go overboard on these supplements—that is why I recommend the tests and consultation with a nutrition specialist. The hair mineral analysis is especially effective since it fluctuates less in its findings than does a blood study. For a modest cost ($35-70), such a test can save you hundreds of dollars on unnecessary vitamin and mineral supplements.

Once you've maximized your training in that last 100 days or so, you should train for 30 days and then rest completely for 4 or 5. You don't want mental staleness or any other form of negativity around when you're training that hard, and the 4 or 5 days off that you allow yourself are a great refresher. The ideal training schedule for the last week before a contest is this: train heavy on Monday, light on Tuesday, *very* light on Wednesday, posing practice with *no* training on Thursday and Friday. This sets you up to achieve your best overall pump on Saturday, the day of the contest.

Training Partners

To become a champion, it is most important to train hard to achieve your highest goals. Goals are necessary because they give us something to work toward. Whenever you set a goal for anything, you must also map out the road for maximum achievement. Personally, I have found that one of my tools for reaching each of my bodybuilding goals has been by training with the right training partner.

When you and your partner work together, the results can be astonishing. Arnold and I have trained together since we first met several years ago in Europe. We always had fun training, setting up a competition between us so that we pushed each other to our maximum. We made a game out of training and looked forward to each session in the gym.

If we didn't feel like training, we would leave the gym and have breakfast or dinner instead. The next day we would have more energy and train very hard. Many bodybuilders are too rigid and set up too strict a program. If they miss one workout they beat themselves down and become depressed or nervous. Arnold and I always kept our schedules flexible. Whenever a contest was approaching we trained at full power and always pushed each other to the maximum; however, if we missed a workout we never became paranoid and felt guilty. We just thought that we would work harder the next day.

There are several things to consider when looking for a good training partner. You should be of about equal strength, have the same motivation and desires of becoming champions. The worst type of training partner is one who has a negative personality. This type of individual can pull you down and drain you of vital energy that you need for training.

One of the reasons that Arnold got in good shape was through me. I pushed him into heavy weights by going into them myself and he was forced to follow me. He motivated me because I would get lazy. He would make me do extra sets when I did not feel like it.

It is also beneficial to be friends with your training partner because you can assist each other should either of you have a problem, such as an injury or illness, or if you just need some encouragement. Should you train for competition, your training partner can

Always be sure that your training partner (in this photo, Jusup Wilkosz) is pushing the weights in the right direction.

help you because he knows you well and knows your weak points as well as your strong points. You should be able to give each other constructive criticism because it is impossible to evaluate your physique or posing routine with only a mirror.

I don't believe in having a training partner actually help you to lift a weight. For the sake of safety, he should be there to remove the weight if it's going to fall on your chest or throat. But if he helps you to lift a weight to help finish a certain number of reps, you don't really gain anything. You may even become dependent on your training partner, and then you cannot train alone. His being there is like having control over your mind and body. If you can't lift the weight another time, you shouldn't pretend—with the help of a partner—that you can. You can't fool your muscles.

Sometimes, I would be doing bench presses while Arnold would spot for me. I would have a hard time with, say, the fifth rep and he would say that I didn't do it right, do it again. I would try and collapse, with the weight on my chest. He would leave the gym. Really! He knew that I would find the strength to lift the weight off. He also would know when to stay in the gym and help me. That is what I mean by finding the right partner!

For a beginner, it is important to know that you need a spotter for bench presses and squats. That's about all as far as safety is

Concentration and stamina are necessary for muscle growth. Your partner should not distract, but help you to concentrate.

Your partner should not be afraid of pushing you hard to make extra repetitions. Arnold knows Franco too well to let him slough off.

A partner with a good sense of humor can help ease the tension of a hard workout without disrupting your routine.

Franco has been just as important to Arnold's many successes as Arnold has been to Franco's.

Sharing dreams: two strangers in a strange land, who have made their wildest dreams come true.

concerned. A partner will be able to use the Exercise Glossary at the back of this book to make sure that you are using proper form for all exercises and that you are not injuring yourself by using improper form or too much weight. Most important, though, your partner must pay attention to you and not distract you from putting your best, most intense effort into every exercise. If you do the same for your partner, you will both benefit tremendously.

Attitude

Now you should be ready to begin a bodybuilding program. I have told you all you need to know about weight training equipment. I hope you have learned how important it is to know about anatomy in general and how it applies to you and your efforts in bodybuilding. This knowledge of equipment and anatomy is just the start for you. Once you begin training, your body will teach you the rest. A good training partner can be of tremendous benefit as long as he can be honest with his encouragement and criticism, and as long as neither of you becomes dependent upon the other.

With the proper training program, you will notice results immediately. As a beginner, you should be able to feel your training working even before you can actually see the re-

Chapter 3

TRAINING PROGRAMS

Weight training and bodybuilding have excellent purposes beyond the mere development of muscles. Both sexes can not only improve their appearances, but enhance both their general health and their abilities for other sports.

So for the bodybuilder who is not interested in the contest aspects of the sport there are two sensible approaches to training. One is simply to establish a good well-rounded program and exercise as many times a week as you care to. There will always be some improvements for you to enjoy. The second approach is to write down specific goals that you wish to complete. Be sure that your goals are within reason. Next map out your plan for achieving your goals by indicating specific exercise routines and a nutritional program. Each time you reach your specific goal work toward another.

To avoid boredom you periodically should have new stimuli. Otherwise your training will become too mechanical and at some point you will tend to slack off. Therefore, move on to another challenge. And either revise your present program or move on to a new level of sets and reps.

On any given day, you should begin your training with stretching exercises, do all your exercises with weights for that day, and then your abdominal exercises. I know there are plenty of books around advising you to begin with those abdominal exercises to get them over with quickly, but that is not good advice. The reason you shouldn't train your waist first is that your body will still be relatively cold. The efforts you put into those early sets really go toward warming your body. Therefore, if you do abdominal exercises first, you won't burn off enough fat, which is the main purpose of the exercise. Once you've begun to sweat and grow tired, as you surely will in lifting weights, fat begins to burn off.

You can make abdominal exercises exciting by setting challenges for yourself. No matter how much development you enjoy in other muscle groups, that washboard look in your waistline always makes everything look that much better. So work your waist hard, and do it correctly and in proper sequence. It's good for your posture, your discipline, and your health.

I will now present training programs for novice bodybuilders. Although these programs are designed specifically for men, they can be modified for use by women (as will be explained in Chapter 5). I have prepared these programs with a great deal of care; they will take you through beginning and intermediate levels to advanced routines. As we get into these programs, you will see that bodybuilding, like other sports, has its own language. Each complete movement is called a repetition, or *rep,* and a number of consecutive repetitions is called a *set.* To know how much weight you need to use when the program says to do 10 reps, for example, the weight should be heavy enough so you can only do 10.

Beginning Level Program

This program should be done 3 times per week for 4–6 weeks. By that time, you will be seeing improvements, and will be ready for something a little more challenging. Begin with two stretching exercises (see Exercise Glossary, pages 121–186):

1. The *back leg stretch* simply involves placing the back of your leg on a bench and stretching toward your toes, as dancers do; this will stretch your hamstring, calf, and lower back regions. *Do 10 repetitions (reps) for each leg, two times (sets) each.*

BEGINNING LEVEL PROGRAM

Clean and press—2 sets, 15 reps. Form is of utmost importance. Bend knees and keep your body erect. Do not bend your spine. (129)

Lateral raises—2 sets, 12–15 reps. Don't be afraid to increase the weight somewhat and "rock" your trunk slightly during this move. (146)

Triceps extension—3 sets, 15 reps. Note that I recommend fewer sets for the biceps than the triceps—that's the correct way to train your arms. This surprises many athletes, but the triceps is an extensor muscle and is bigger and longer than the biceps; thus it needs more work. Keeping both the triceps and biceps balanced prevents injuries in the shoulders and elbows. (182)

Lunges—2 sets, 15 reps for each leg. These can be done with a pair of light dumbbells, or no weight at all to start; simply take a giant step forward and then return to starting position. (151)

Continue to the waist and abdominal exercises described next. Your metabolism should be revved up and ready to burn off that spare tire around your midriff.

Crunch sit-ups—2 sets, 25 reps. I recommend you do one set of each of these and the following exercises in rotation, then go back and start again. It's the least taxing routine from a mental point of view; equally important, it works your waistline from many different angles at the same time. (132)

Bent-leg raises—2 sets, 25 reps. This is an excellent exercise. It protects the spine from the problems that are caused by straight leg raises. (124)

Leg raises—2 sets, 25 reps on each side. (150)

Franco lifting 525 pounds—a new world's record for the bench press.

2. *Standing side bends*—standing with arms on your waist and with feet about a yard apart, bend to each side. *Do 10 repetitions (reps) for each side, alternating back and forth, two times.*

Your weight training begins at this point. For the most part, these are fundamental exercises. Page numbers are given in parentheses so you can refer to the Exercise Glossary for a detailed explanation of how to do each exercise.

Return to the same two stretching exercises you began with and do one set of each, 10 reps for each leg or side. If time permits, go for a good brisk mile run. The benefits of running have been discussed in a thousand other books; its importance here is as a waistline trimmer and an all-around muscle definer for the lower body. For maximum results, run after, not before, you train.

Intermediate Level Program

Within 4–6 weeks you will be looking and feeling much better. Everything will be ready for you to map out a new goal. Your technique, strength, and general appearance will be conditioned enough to rapidly move onward into the intermediate level for novice bodybuilders.

You should add another day for training and follow this program for four days. You will still be training your entire body in one day; however, this program will prepare you for dividing the body parts for the advanced level programs.

If you miss training for one or two sessions, just go back to the gym and continue with this program. Because your body has rested for a few days, you should try heavier weights. Thus, you will have a harder workout. As I mentioned in Chapter 2, when Arnold and I were training together, we decided not to train on several occasions and had breakfast. Instead of feeling guilty, we remained positive about ourselves and thought that we deserved a rest. The next time we trained, we were able to work harder and accomplish more. I can't stress this enough:

Always keep a positive mental attitude and acknowledge each gain. Guilt and negativity will only pull you down.

During this intermediate level program, try to increase the amounts of weight you lift and force the training more. This program should continue for 2-3 months. Then move on to the advanced level program.

Intermediate Level Exercises

Research has proven that the lack of proper stretching is the main cause of sports injuries. Therefore, it is most important to begin with the stretching exercises from the beginning level program (back leg stretch and standing side bends). Again, numbers in parentheses refer to the Exercise Glossary where full descriptions of exercises are presented.

When your training is completed, hang for 2-3 minutes from the chinning bar to stretch your spine and muscles to relieve compression of the spine, which can result from heavy weight training.

INTERMEDIATE LEVEL PROGRAM

Bench press—The first set of this exercise should be done with light weight for 20 reps as a warm-up, then increase weight. Do 3 more sets of 15 reps. This is one of the best exercises for the entire upper body. (123)

Dips—3 sets, 10 reps. Rest less than one minute between sets. (134)

Pulldowns—3 sets, 12 reps. Use a wide grip. This exercise is good for the lower back. (158-9)

One-arm rowing—2 sets, 10 reps for each arm. Be sure to pull the weight all the way up and feel the full movement. (154)

Bent-over lateral raises—3 sets, 12 reps. Keep your elbows out and don't bend too far forward. Make sure you feel it in the rhomboideus and back deltoids. (125-6)

Lateral raises—3 sets, 12 reps. Bend your elbows slightly and keep your palms down. (146)

Triceps extension—3 sets, 12 reps. Elbows should be between 10-14 inches apart and get a full extension movement. (182)

Triceps pushdown—3 sets, 10 reps. Place elbows close to your body. (182)

Seated dumbbell curls—3 sets, 10 reps. Be sure to turn wrists so your palms are up with a good contraction. (164-5)

Incline dumbbell curls—2 sets, 10 reps. Begin with your palms inward and turn them outward on the way up. (144)

Leg extensions—3 sets, 25 reps. Extend the leg completely, feel a short burn, and concentrate. (148)

Squat—3 sets, 15 reps. Look forward, keep your body erect, bend your knees forward, and keep your feet straight. (173)

Lunges—1 set, 10 reps for each leg. Make sure that your body is erect at all times. (151)

Calf raises—4 sets, 20 repetitions. If possible do calf raises without bending your knees and move up and down as much as possible. (177)

Do the following waist and abdominal movements in combination; that is, move from one exercise to the next with no rest between sets.
Bent-leg sit-ups—2 sets, 25 reps. (124)
Crunch sit-ups—2 sets, 25 reps. (132)
Leg raises—2 sets, 25 reps. (150)
Bent-leg raises—2 sets, 25 reps. (124)

Advanced Level Program

With this advanced level program you can achieve champion status. This applies to amateurs as well as to professionals. I trained with this program and won the Mr. Universe title and several of my students also have won major titles with it.

As you begin this program, you should also begin to monitor your diet more closely. Research has indicated that, as you increase your training, you must also increase your intake of calories. You need additional amounts of complex (unrefined) carbohydrates to give you more energy for training. You also will need more protein foods *(not protein powder)* for building and repairing muscle cells.

Other nutrient supplements might be considered. For example, chelated multiple minerals should be substantially increased as

Deadlifts require handling heavy poundages and extra long barbell bars.

Alternating arms on front raises allows you to concentrate all of your efforts on one arm at a time.

T-bar rowing for fun and profit before the camera crew of PUMPING IRON.

It's always good practice to watch your exercise form in front of a mirror both to check your form and to visualize muscle growth.

Hanging from a chinning bar after heavy-duty press exercises is good for your spine.

you train more, because you will require more minerals to train the muscles more efficiently. Every time you increase your protein intake you need more minerals. Vitamin B-12 should be increased because your liver is working harder to manufacture and store more glycogen. Vitamin B-6 should be increased because B-6 aids in food assimilation, and in protein and fat metabolism. Furthermore, it is necessary for synthesizing protein into amino acids. Good digestive enzyme supplements that contain HCl (hydrochloric acid) should be taken to break down and digest the increased protein. To prevent dehydration, and to improve the transport of nutrients and the elimination of bodily waste, at least 8–10 glasses of water should be drunk daily.

Advanced Level Exercise Routine (Series One)

This advanced level program is designed to divide your body part training into two-day workouts. Ideally, you should train your upper body and stomach on Mondays and Thursdays, your lower body and stomach on Tuesdays and Fridays, and take Wednesday off completely. Wednesday, Saturday, and Sunday are recuperation days. This program can be used indefinitely. However, if you wish to compete, after a few months you should proceed into superset training.

As for the previous programs, numbers in parentheses refer to full descriptions given in the Exercise Glossary.

ADVANCED LEVEL PROGRAM I

Monday and Thursday

1. Back leg stretch—2 sets, 10 reps. (121)
2. Side bends—2 sets, 20 reps. (168)
3. Bench press—5 sets, 10 reps. (123)
4. Incline bench—3 sets, 10 reps. (143)
5. Dips—3 sets, 10 reps. (134)
6. Chins in front of neck—5 sets, 10 reps. (127)
7. Barbell rowing (or T-bar rowing)—3 sets, 10 reps. (122, 181)
8. One-arm rowing—2 sets, 10 reps. (154)
9. Bent-over lateral raises—4 sets, 10 reps. (125–6)
10. Lateral raises—4 sets, 10 reps, with dumbbells or cables. (146)
11. Standing dumbbell presses—2 sets, 20 reps. (179)
12. Lying triceps extensions—5 sets, 12 reps. (153)
13. Triceps pushdowns—4 sets, 12 reps. (182)
14. Seated dumbbell curls—4 sets, 12 reps. (164–5)
15. Preacher's bench curls—3 sets, 10 reps.* (156)

Then do your customary four-set rotation of abdominal exercises.

16. Bent-leg sit-ups—4 sets, 25 reps; in rotation with next three exercises. (124)
17. Crunches—4 sets, 25 reps; in rotation. (132)
18. Leg raises—4 sets, 25 reps; in rotation. (150)
19. Lying side leg raises—4 sets, 25 reps; in rotation. (152)

*Again, notice that we're doing nine sets for triceps (exercises 12 and 13), but only seven sets of curls (exercises 14 and 15) for biceps.

Tuesday and Friday

1. Back leg stretch—2 sets, 10 reps. (121)
2. Side bends—2 sets, 20 reps. (168)
3. Lunges—3 sets, 10 reps for each leg. (151)
4. Leg extensions—4 sets, 25 reps. (148)
5. Leg curls—2 sets, 25 reps. We do fewer sets for the hamstrings than for the quadriceps; this assists in preventing knee injuries. (147)
6. Squat—5 sets, 10 reps, going from light weight to as heavy as you can safely handle. (173)
7. Calf raises—7 sets, 15 reps. (170, 177)
8. Front calf raise—5 sets, 15 reps. (139)
9. Bent-leg sit-ups—4 sets, 25 reps; in rotation. (124)
10. Crunches—4 sets, 25 reps; in rotation. (132)
11. Leg raises—4 sets, 25 reps; in rotation. (150)
12. Lying side leg raises—4 sets, 25 reps; in rotation. (152)

Note that I recommend repeating your abdominal exercises on all four workout days. You can either run after training or, if you prefer, you may run on another day, following your own schedule. I personally have found running very good for bodybuilding, but it should be limited to less than three miles and no more than three times a week. If you run more than that, the muscles in your upper body will lose size.

Do two stretching stints on the chinning bar for two minutes or so each stint. Remember to bend your legs; it aids in decompressing the spine after training, particularly after squatting exercises.

Advanced Level Exercise Routine (Series Two)

I have found that to continue muscle growth and increase your power, the muscles have to be worked and stimulated in different ways. I suggest that every 2-4 months you alternate your advanced level training routine with this training routine. This routine is for training six times per week, dividing the body parts into three two-day workouts. It is very important to follow this program in the order or sequence in which it is presented.

The following chart includes the standard notation for listing sets and reps used by most

ADVANCED LEVEL PROGRAM II

Monday and Thursday

Chest
Bench press—3 × 8, 2 × 6, 1 × 4, 1 × 4
Incline bench press—4 × 10
Dips—4 × 15
Flyes—3 × 8 (137)

Back
Chins behind the neck—4 × 10
Chins in front of the neck—5 × 10
T-bar rowing—4 × 8
Pulley rowing—4 × 8 (160)

Calves
Donkey raises—5 × 15 (136)
Calf raises—4 × 15
Bent-leg raises—4 × 25
Lying side bends—4 × 25
Leg stretch—4 × 25
Bent-leg sit-ups—4 × 25

Tuesday and Friday

Shoulders
Bent-over lateral raises—5 × 10
Lateral raises, with dumbbells or cables—5 × 8
Press behind the neck—3 × 8 (157)
Front raises—3 × 8 (139, 140)

Arms
Lying triceps extensions—5 × 10
Seated dumbbell curls—4 × 8
Triceps pushdowns—5 × 10
Preacher's bench curl—5 × 8
Sitting triceps extensions—4 × 10 (169)
Concentration curl—2 × 8 (130)

Forearms
Wrist curl—3 × 10

Stomach
Bent-leg sit-ups—4 × 25
Bent-leg raises—4 × 25
Lying side leg raises—4 × 25

Wednesday and Saturday

Thighs
Leg extension—5 × 25
Squat—5 × 10
Leg presses—4 × 25 (149)
Leg curl—3 × 25

Calves
Donkey raises—7 × 15
Calf raises—3 × 15

Stomach
Crunch sit-ups—3 × 25
End each training session with hamstring stretches—1 × 10 (slow) (142)

professional bodybuilders. For example, "4 × 8" simply means "4 sets, 8 reps" as was presented in previous charts. When you see a series of such numbers (e.g., "4 × 8, 3 × 6, 2 × 4, 1 × 2"), it indicates that you should begin with light weight and increase poundages as you decrease sets and reps. When a bracket ({) is used on the chart beside two or more exercise names, it indicates that you should alternate exercises from set to set—just as you rotated exercises for the waist and abdominal movements in the previous programs.

Before you look at the second advanced routine, I have one more thing to tell you: It is the exact program I used prior to training for my Mr. Olympia victories.

The Bodybuilding Lifestyle

I am certain that sometime in the first 4-6 weeks of using my beginning level program, you will notice a difference in your life. Your body may well ache from the stress of weight training, but it will also vibrate with strength and vitality. You will look and feel better—you will feel like a bodybuilder. You will begin to look forward to your training sessions and to learning how each exercise affects your appearance. You will come to agree with me that there is nothing more important for you than a nutritious diet, a positive attitude, and hard training.

By the time you have finished the intermediate level of training, you will have a new body that will make you proud, that will make people look twice when they see you, and that will open doors for you that once were closed. When you reach the advanced levels, you can prepare yourself for a long and healthy life, because you will have begun the bodybuilding lifestyle.

If you go no farther than the advanced level programs described in this chapter, you will be able to maintain your new body without being a slave to the program. You can lay off for a couple of weeks and quickly pick up where you left off. Just remember that the longer you keep up a rigorous training schedule, the longer it will take for you to lose your shape if you should stop—unless you go on some kind of binge. But you won't want to stop once you see what your body can become and once you feel the vibrant, clean excitement of the bodybuilding lifestyle.

MR. EUROPA 1970
79
74
75
ATHLETIK

1
2
19
75
3

Chapter 4
PROFESSIONAL BODYBUILDING

You should now know a lot about training—what works for you and what doesn't. For many people who have reached the advanced level of bodybuilding, maintaining their health and fitness will be an end in itself. They will be in the top 25 percent of the world's population who are in excellent condition and who—barring some unfortunate accident—can look forward to a longer life expectancy than the other 75 percent. But there will be some advanced bodybuilders who want more; they want their particular body condition and training techniques validated through competition. Bodybuilding contests arose because of the need for this validation.

To become a professional bodybuilder, you must now learn the special techniques and tricks that will allow you to maximize your bodybuilding results in the minimum amount of time, to utilize equipment more wisely, and to refine your eating habits so you get maximum results from your training. You must begin to make up your own training programs by recognizing what your body needs most.

In this chapter, I will explain how you can personalize the training programs from the last chapter, so you can train for competition. I will present techniques and several training programs that I used to win the 1981 Mr. Olympia contest. I will explain what happens at contests and give you strategies that I have used for successful training and successful posing. Most important, I will help you to become confident by explaining what good sportsmanship is all about.

But before I start on these things, I want you to put aside all your worries about competing. You are probably thinking that being a professional bodybuilder is a full-time job and that you will have to be in the gym all day long. This is not true. Let me tell you what is, perhaps, my greatest secret about professional bodybuilding: If all you do is eat, sleep, and train, you will never win.

Throughout my career I have been busy doing other things besides training for, and winning, contests. I studied for, and received, a license in chiropractic and a Ph.D. in Nutrition. I give seminars, write articles and books, and appear in commercials, television shows, and movies. Everything I do, I do because I want to and because these things are fun for me. My mind never dwells on whether I have to do one more set of exercises to improve a muscle or whether I will win a contest.

Letting your mind dwell on any one thing too long is not good for you. It can destroy your image of yourself and your mental attitude. Look at it this way: If you can qualify to be in a contest, you are probably in better condition than 90–95 percent of the people in the world. You are a champion going against other champions. What can give you an edge in such a competition is knowing, too, that you can do other things and that you are *more* than a bodybuilder. Winning a contest will make you feel great, but it shouldn't be the only thing in your life that will make you feel great.

Bodybuilding is a great sport. It takes a tremendous discipline to get in shape because that is a human being's biggest problem, I believe. No one wants to put forth that kind of effort. A champion bicyclist or football player trains hard, but look at what kind of shape they are in. The bicyclist has big legs and very skinny arms—very unhealthy in the upper body because most of his or her circulation is down in the legs. Football players may be more rounded out, physically, but look at the chances for becoming injured. When you look at most sports, you see that even the greatest players retire while in their thirties—many of them just wear themselves out.

After 3 years of dedicated weight training, Franco won his first Mr. Universe title.

I am 40 and am still going strong. I suffered an injured leg five years ago and the doctors told me my career was over. I proved them wrong by winning the 1981 Mr. Olympia. I was 40 years old, but my skin tone looked like 20—I would have lost if that were not so.

So set aside your worries about professional bodybuilding. It is a great sport that has advantages over all the others: You are your own manager, you can call your own hours, you are among the healthiest group of people in the world, and you can, with hard work and determination, be a champion among champions.

Now I will tell you how to do it!

Training Techniques

Supersets

Supersetting two or more exercises is a technique for training two muscles at the same time instead of one, specifically, two *antagonistic* (opposite) muscles. Antagonistic muscles or muscle groups are those which work *against* each other in a coordinated movement. For instance, the biceps is a *flexor* muscle and the triceps is an *extensor,* or muscle that extends. The biceps work to *flex* the elbow, while the triceps work to *straighten,* or extend, it out again. A reasonable superset routine that exercises both muscles at once will produce striking results.

Properly matching the muscles is the first and most important rule of supersetting. You must select exercises that not only match, but also help balance antagonistic pairs of muscles. Sensible matches include chest-back (and, for added variety, chest-shoulders, and back-shoulders), biceps-triceps, anterior-posterior forearm muscles, anterior-posterior deltoids, quads-hamstrings in your thighs, and front-back calf muscles.

Realistically, the abdomen cannot be supersetted with any other muscle group. Thus, for any training routine you devise on your own, continue your stomach training as before: 4 exercises in rotation, 4 sets of 25 reps each for each exercise.

The second most important aspect of the supersets technique—after you've decided on appropriate exercises—is to do the two exercises with as little rest in between as possible. *No* rest is ideal, but you may well find that your supersets routine requires you to decrease the weight slightly at the beginning; however, after a few workouts you will increase the weight.

Note that in the following recommended

SUPERSET ROUTINE

Mondays and Thursdays
Chest, back, shoulders, calves, stomach

Bench press—5 × 8; alternate with chins in back of neck, 4 × 10 (or as many as you can)
Incline bench—4 × 10; plus chins in front of neck, 5 × 10
Dips—4 × 15; with T-bar rowing, 4 × 10
Flyes—3 × 10; with pulley rowing, 3 × 10
Bent-over lateral raises—5 × 10; with press behind the neck, 4 × 10
Lateral raises—5 × 10; with upright rowing, 4 × 10
Calf raises—7 × 15; with front calf raises, 4 × 15. A good example of the flexor-extensor principle.
Stomach—sit-ups, leg raises, and side leg raises in rotation, 4 × 25 each. Add side bends if the sides of your waist are not cut enough.

Tuesdays and Fridays
Arms, forearms, stomach

Pushdowns—5 × 12; with dumbbell curls, 4 × 10
Lying triceps extensions—5 × 12; with incline dumbbell curl or barbell curl, 4 × 10
Narrow grip bench press—4 × 10 (153); with preacher's bench, 4 × 10
Triceps push-ups—2 × 10 (183); with one-arm concentration curl or barbell curl, 2 × 10
Forearm (wrist) curl (palms up)—3 × 15 (186); with forearm (reverse wrist) curl (palms down), 3 × 15 (163)
Stomach—repeat stomach routine from Mondays and Thursdays.

Wednesdays and Saturdays
Thighs, calves, stomach

Leg extensions—6 × 25; with leg curls, 5 × 25
Lunges—3 × 25; with squats, 5 × 10
Donkey raises—7 × 20; with front calf raises, 4 × 20
Stomach—as before.

routines, the number of *sets* may not match exactly. For instance, I suggest 6 sets of leg extensions supersetted with only 5 sets of leg curls. I have done so by design, the objective being to balance structure and strength. Most people are stronger in the flexor muscles than in the extensors; ideally, the two muscles should be considerably closer to equal. For a simple demonstration of this inequality, observe how much more power and flexibility you have in turning your hand down—that is, in the direction of the palm—than you do in turning it back toward the wrist. Your entire superset routine should follow the principle of adjusting the number of sets for certain exercises to correct imbalances in structure and strength of antagonistic muscles or muscle groups.

This program will thoroughly exercise every major muscle group twice weekly, and the abdomen and calves four times each.

Split Routines

Split routine training, like supersets, assigns different body parts to different days. A simple example of this would be six workouts a week, three for the upper body and three for the lower, with stomach exercises on at least five of those days. Even better is five workouts a week, staggering them so you get three upper-body and two lower-body workouts in one week and just the reverse in the next. The five-day breakdown is an optimum combination of exercise and rest.

Trisets. Once you reach the advanced level of bodybuilding, you will almost certainly hear about trisets. This means exercising three different muscles in rotation—for example, the front, back, and top of the shoulders can be worked out in rotation through bench presses, chins, and lateral raises. Except for the time saved in doing

60–90-DAY BLITZ ROUTINE

Monday and Thursday
Morning (Chest, back, stomach)

Bench press—5 × 8
Incline bench press—4 × 8
Dips— 4 × 12
Flyes—3 × 10
Chins behind the neck—5 × 10
Chins front—5 × 10
T-bar rowing—4 × 10
Pulley—4 × 10
Crunches—4 × 25
Bent-leg sit-ups—4 × 25
Lying side leg raises—4 × 25

Evening (Shoulders, calves)

Bent-over lateral raises—4 × 10
Lateral raises—4 × 10
Press behind the neck—3 × 10
Front raises—3 × 10
Donkey raises—7 × 15
Calf raises—5 × 10

Tuesday and Friday
(Arms)

Incline dumbbell curl—5 × 10
Triceps pushdowns—5 × 10
Lying triceps extension—5 × 10
Dumbbell curl—4 × 10
Sitting incline barbell extensions—5 × 10
Preacher's bench—4 × 10

Wednesday and Saturday
(Thighs, calves, stomach)

Leg extensions— 5 × 20
Leg curl—4 × 20
Squat—5 × 10
Leg press—4 × 20
Donkey raises—7 × 15
Calf raises—5 × 10
Crunches—4 × 25
Bent-leg raises—4 × 25
Side leg raises—4 × 25

trisets, there is little benefit to be gained from doing them, because you must use lighter weights and you end up spreading your blood to too many areas at the same time.

Double Split. Prior to competition I have used the double split routine. To obtain maximum results, I trained the bigger body parts in the morning at full power. In the afternoon, I did a lighter workout of smaller body parts, using less time than in the morning. This type of double split allows recuperation for the body and gets desired results in the shortest time without overtraining. There are advantages and disadvantages to the double split routine. I will explain them so that you understand both.

It takes approximately 48 hours to replenish and store the glycogen that the body uses for energy. In a double split routine the glycogen storage becomes depleted and the natural resistance of the body becomes weakened. This weakened condition is also known as overtraining, and your bodybuilding gains can begin to reverse themselves. Muscle growth stops and the desire to train greatly diminishes. A general fatigue can develop, along with muscle weakness and increased irritability. These conditions can lead to training accidents and injury. Furthermore, your natural resistance becomes lowered and the body becomes more vulnerable to infection.

Of the thousands of people who have consulted me for various training problems—including patients of my chiropractic center—at least half of them had problems because of overtraining.

This is why you must always set realistic goals and stay relaxed. The more anxious you become, the quicker your body goes into reverse. Acknowledge each gain you make and know that you are progressing. Avoid comparing yourself to anyone else. You are an individual with an entirely unique structure and metabolism, and you will respond differently to the same diet and training program than other bodybuilders. Be sure to keep your competitive spirit healthy or you will become negative, and negative energy can only cause problems.

My Mr. Olympia Blitz Routine

Previously, I discussed how I timed my training so that I reached peak form for a contest. I used a routine that combines the double split routine and split routine in a six-day workout. I recommend you use this routine anywhere from 60–90 days before a contest. Keep in mind that you should have balanced out all of your weak muscle groups first and that these numbers are not automatically going to work for you as well as they have worked for me. You will need to adjust them to ensure that you keep a well-proportioned shape to your body.

Training Strategy

To win most bodybuilding contests, you must develop all the muscles in your body to their utmost *without losing proportions.* You can have mighty arms and shoulders, and thoroughly ripped abdominals, but if your thighs and calves are not proportionately enlarged, then you will lose. In the Mr. Olympia contest, however, perfect proportions are not enough. You need extra things that the other contestants cannot get.

Throughout this and the following sections of this chapter are photos of me posing in many different positions. They were taken around the times of my Mr. Olympia victories, when I was in peak condition. These are to illustrate points about posing as well as to demonstrate perfect proportion and those "extra things" I just mentioned, such as the heart-shaped split in my biceps, the split across my chest, and the split in my calves.

In discussing strategy, I am really telling you about the difference between the advanced bodybuilder and the professional bodybuilder. The professional must look at his competition to see which of his own muscles need special emphasis during training. For example, I didn't want to beat Chris Dickerson just on overall looks, I wanted to beat him on his best body part. So I trained my calves so they not only looked equally developed

Just as wind and sea create striations in rocks, you, the bodybuilder, can create such lines in your body until it resembles rock. This process is often called "bodysculpting."

Look at the difference five years can make! He isn't getting older, he's getting better. Leaner, yet more defined, the Franco on the left won the 1981 Mr. Olympia, the one on the right won the 1976 Mr. Olympia.

You can hardly tell that, fully pumped, Franco is straining hard in this front lat spray pose.

The side-back pose. Note how right calf is further tensed by lifting foot up onto toes.

nore radical version of the side-back pose—Franco's 1981
sion.

Competition forces you to hone your posing skill, which is the most creative aspect of bodybuilding.

This side chest shot not only shows the judges how well developed Franco's chest is, but shows his chest with other body parts flexed so that they see it in proportion to the rest of his body.

inside and out, but with a split in the middle that showed greater definition in my calves than in Chris Dickerson's calves.

So you see, competing against other bodybuilders makes you look at them to determine what their strengths and weaknesses are so you can beat them in every body part. You shouldn't just build size and proportion to your muscles; you must develop definition. It's not so hard—it's the best thing about professional bodybuilding. You will begin to see little muscles, striations in muscle groups, or something about your body that is unique. Then, you will work on those special details because you want the judges at a contest to see what makes you stand out among other bodybuilders. These differences are why you must pay attention to what you are doing during each and every workout, so you will see which exercise brings out the unique muscular details that can make you a winning bodybuilder.

I will tell you more about my strategy for winning the 1981 Mr. Olympia, but first I need to discuss posing. If you are serious about competitive bodybuilding, you must learn about posing.

Posing

Posing plays an essential role in developing your mental attitude about bodybuilding training. Your body responds to your mind; therefore, you must concentrate not only on training but on how you want your body to look. Form a mental picture of exactly how you want to look and keep going over this in your mind. The most effective time to do this is while your brain is in the alpha state—just before sleep and immediately upon awakening.

Always concentrate on all of your good qualities and do not dwell on your weak points. We all have imperfections—the important thing to remember is not to let the negative aspects of your physique overrule your attitude regarding your positive aspects. Spend your energies working out the weak points rather than on worrying about them.

Posing is the most creative aspect of bodybuilding, and competition provides you a chance to show the world how you have developed your body to its full artistic potential. It *is* an art that must be developed with practice. Many great bodies have lost in competitive situations because the artist-athlete failed to concentrate on his posing. You must learn to show off your best qualities and minimize your weaker points with correct posture and graceful movements. With practice, you can develop your own style without copying someone else's routine.

Probably the most difficult aspect of posing is to monitor your progress in the mirror. After each training session, while you are still pumped, stand in front of a mirror and flex each muscle. Closely observe how each one looks. Notice all the details. Try to determine

which exercises did the most in bringing out details for each muscle. The better you look to yourself, the quicker your body does what you want it to do.

It is difficult to really see yourself from every angle using a mirror. Another valuable tool for posing is to have a set of photographs taken from every angle. Have them taken at least monthly for comparison with previous sets. I also recommend that you have an experienced bodybuilder look closely at you to provide constructive criticism.

Once you have mastered flexing and relaxing the muscles, begin to put a routine together. At first, you might feel awkward, but as you continue to practice, certain poses will become automatic and then all you have to do is refine and polish the moves. Do your routine at the end of every training session and imagine that you are posing in front of thousands of people and that they react positively as your perfect body moves gracefully from one pose to another.

Women bodybuilders are really the masters of posing. Many of them have backgrounds in dance or gymnastics, and their superb routines are proof that such instruction is very helpful. If you have difficulty in posing, perhaps a dancing course or a choreographer will be necessary in perfecting a routine.

Before I discuss posing at contests, I want to make sure you avoid a big problem that posing creates. The strain of contracting a muscle group to its maximum causes a great many athletes to make a face. So many athletes do so, in fact, that only five top-flight bodybuilders have ever been able to pose completely without grimacing: Arnold, Sergio Oliva, Frank Zane, Reg Park, and myself. Such grimacing causes blood to go to your face. Not only do you look red-faced, but you attract the negative attention of the judges with your new blush. And most important, that blood is coming out of your pump, where you need it the most.

We all have about 6 liters of blood in our bodies. If, say, half a liter rushes to your face—and that's a reasonable estimate—you've spent close to 10 percent of your total blood supply in order to achieve a negative effect.

It's not easy to keep your face relaxed

This sequence of poses demonstrates how simple changes of position can make dramatic differences.

during muscle contractions; however, the more you practice, the easier and more automatic it becomes.

Posing at Contests

The standard IFBB (International Federation of Bodybuilders) judging structure consists of five stages or rounds. Seven judges chosen by the IFBB participate and can award up to 20 points to any athlete during each of the first three rounds. The maximum number of points a bodybuilder can get after these three rounds is 300. (The lowest and highest scores are disregarded to ensure fairness of scores, thus five scores of 20 [100] times three rounds equals 300.) In the fourth round, each judge is allowed to award one point to one

MR. OLYMPIA

ROUND	NAME	COUNTRY	JUDGES' MARKS: Jacques Blommaert Belgium	Jim Manion USA	Winston Roberts Canada	Sven-Ole Thorsen Denmark	Franco Fassi Italy	Dominic Certo USA	Doug Evans Wales	TOTAL
FIRST	Franco Columbu	USA	18	19	19	19	20	19	20	96
	Chris Dickerson	USA	18	18	20	20	19	19	20	96
	Tom Platz	USA	20	19	19	19	19	20	19	96
	Roy Callender	Canada	19	19	19	18	19	20	18	94
	Danny Padilla	USA	19	20	20	17	19	18	19	95
	Jusup Wilkosz	Germany	19	18	18	18	18	19	17	91
	Dennis Tinerino	USA	16	18	18	15	18	18	18	88
	Johnny Fuller	England	17	18	18	17	17	18	18	88
	Samir Bannout	USA	17	17	17	15	18	18	17	86
	Roger Walker	Australia	17	17	18	16	18	18	18	88
	Hubert Metz	Germany	16	16	17	14	17	18	16	82
	Carlos Rodriguez	USA	16	16	16	12	16	17	16	80
	Ed Corney	USA	16	15	17	12	17	17	16	81
	Steve Davis	USA	15	15	16	13	16	17	15	77
	Mike Katz	USA	16	16	16	13	14	17	15	77
	Ken Waller	USA	15	16	16	13	14	17	15	76
	Jorma Raty	Finland	15	15	14	15	17	16	17	78
SECOND	Franco Columbu	USA	18	20	19	20	20	20	20	99
	Chris Dickerson	USA	18	19	20	20	19	19	19	96
	Tom Platz	USA	19	19	19	19	19	20	20	96
	Roy Callender	Canada	20	19	20	19	19	19	19	96
	Danny Padilla	USA	19	19	19	18	19	18	19	94
	Jusup Wilkosz	Germany	18	18	18	18	18	19	17	90
	Dennis Tinerino	USA	16	18	18	15	18	18	18	88
	Johnny Fuller	England	16	18	18	17	18	18	18	89
	Samir Bannout	USA	17	17	17	16	18	18	17	86
	Roger Walker	Australia	17	17	18	16	18	18	17	87
	Hubert Metz	Germany	18	16	18	15	17	18	17	86
	Carlos Rodriguez	USA	17	17	16	13	17	18	17	84
	Ed Corney	USA	16	15	16	13	16	17	17	80
	Steve Davis	USA	16	16	16	14	17	17	15	80
	Mike Katz	USA	15	16	16	14	16	17	16	79
	Ken Waller	USA	15	15	16	14	16	17	16	78
	Jorma Raty	Finland	15	15	15	15	16	16	18	77

ROUND	NAME	COUNTRY	JUDGES' MARKS: Jacques Blommaert Belgium	Jim Manion USA	Winston Roberts Canada	Sven-Ole Thorsen Denmark	Franco Fassi Italy	Dominic Certo USA	Doug Evans Wales	TOTAL	PLACE
THIRD	Franco Columbu	USA	18	20	19	20	20	20	20	99	
	Chris Dickerson	USA	19	19	20	20	19	19	20	97	
	Tom Platz	USA	19	20	18	20	18	20	19	96	
	Roy Callender	Canada	20	19	19	19	19	20	19	96	
	Danny Padilla	USA	18	20	19	18	18	18	19	92	
	Jusup Wilkosz	Germany	19	17	18	18	18	18	17	89	
	Dennis Tinerino	USA	17	18	18	15	18	18	18	89	
	Johnny Fuller	England	16	17	18	17	17	18	18	87	
	Samir Bannout	USA	18	18	19	16	19	18	18	91	
	Roger Walker	Australia	17	17	18	16	17	18	17	86	
	Hubert Metz	Germany	17	16	17	15	17	18	17	84	
	Carlos Rodriguez	USA	17	17	17	13	17	18	17	85	
	Ed Corney	USA	18	17	17	13	18	17	16	85	
	Steve Davis	USA	16	17	18	14	18	17	16	84	
	Mike Katz	USA	16	16	16	14	17	17	16	81	
	Ken Waller	USA	16	16	17	14	16	17	16	81	
	Jorma Raty	Finland	15	16	16	15	16	16	18	79	
POSEDOWN	Franco Columbu	USA					1		1	296	1
	Chris Dickerson	USA			1	1				291	2
	Tom Platz	USA	1					1		290	3
	Roy Callender	Canada								286	4
	Danny Padilla	USA		1						282	5
	Jusup Wilkosz	Germany								270	6
TOTALS	Franco Columbu	USA	54	59	57	59	60	59	60	294	1
	Chris Dickerson	USA	55	56	60	60	57	57	59	289	2
	Tom Platz	USA	58	58	56	58	56	60	58	288	3
	Roy Callender	Canada	59	57	58	56	57	59	56	286	4
	Danny Padilla	USA	56	59	58	53	56	54	57	281	5
	Jusup Wilkosz	Germany	56	53	54	54	54	56	51	270	6
	Dennis Tinerino	USA	49	54	54	45	54	54	54	265	7
	Johnny Fuller	England	49	53	54	51	52	54	54	264	8
	Samir Bannout	USA	52	52	53	47	55	54	52	263	9
	Roger Walker	Australia	51	51	54	48	53	54	52	261	10
	Hubert Metz	Germany	51	48	52	44	51	54	50	252	11
	Carlos Rodriguez	USA	50	50	49	38	50	53	50	249	12
	Ed Corney	USA	50	47	50	38	51	51	49	246	13
	Steve Davis	USA	47	48	50	41	51	51	46	241	14
	Mike Katz	USA	47	48	48	41	47	51	47	237	15
	Ken Waller	USA	46	47	49	41	46	50	47	235	16
	Jorma Raty	Finland	45	46	45	45	49	48	53	234	17

Official scores for the 1981 Mr. Olympia. (Reprinted with permission from MUSCLE & FITNESS magazine.)

athlete. Each point counts in this round, so the highest achievable score is 307. The fifth round is really just for show as you will see from the following round-by-round description:

- Round 1—All contestants appear on stage and, without contractions, stand as they normally would.
- Round 2—Compulsory poses are executed by each contestant, one athlete at a time.
- Round 3—Individual posing routines are presented to the judges.
- Round 4—The judges call forth contestants to strike similar poses for comparison. This is sometimes called the *posedown.*
- Round 5—This round is for the audience to judge their favorites. Usually held on the evening of the contest, it's filled with lights, music, and drama.

Let's take a closer look at each of the five posing rounds and suggest how you can enhance your performance in each.

In the first round, where all contestants stand more or less normally, the judges will take a look at you from the front, side, and back. Even though the rules call for no contractions or poses here, be aware of your posture and presentation. Stand erect and balance your weight correctly on both feet. Poor posture or an imbalanced stance usually is a sign of nervousness and lack of confidence. Always appear confident and solid on the posing platform and keep smiling. Smiling is an essential tool for radiating confidence. When asked to turn so your side is toward the judges keep it slightly open to the judges; it looks better that way. And when turning your back to the judges, spread your lats as much as you can while keeping your arms in—and most important of all, *turn your neck slightly to the judges.* This will flex your trapezius muscles and allow you to maintain eye contact with the judges, two very positive and point-gaining effects.

In the second round, the head judge will call the sequence of compulsory poses desired. And once he does, everybody must do that routine in the same style. The poses are a *front lat spread, double biceps from the front, side chest pose, lat spread from back, double biceps from back, front abdominals* with arms up and one leg extended, *most muscular,* or the crab, and *side view of triceps.* Remember to keep eye contact with the judges for as long as you can without breaking concentration on each pose. Be aware of exactly where the judges are and face them for maximum exposure.

In the third round, you present your individual posing routine for the judges. You and your fellow contestants will be called out in order by contestant numbers (assigned before the judging begins), to execute a posing routine of your choice. Regarding that choice, most good bodybuilders are capable of per-

Front abdominals: a compulsory pose.

Franco performs a series of poses during the third round of the 1981 Mr. Olympia.

forming somewhere between 25 and 35 poses. You ought to be able to bring that down to 15 or so of your very best poses. Be objective about selecting what makes you look your best. And, of course, select a sequence which allows you nice transitional moves between poses. Never forget to maintain eye contact and to keep smiling.

Posing routines are usually accompanied by music. You will have prerecorded the music and have given tapes to the proper show technician to be played during your routine. The selection of posing music is strictly an individual matter. The main thing here is to select something that you are comfortable with and that suits your personality. Do not be concerned about what someone else has selected; stick to your preference.

In the fourth round, the last phase of afternoon competition, the judges will call from five to seven of the highest-scoring contestants to execute the same pose. You should attain the best pump you can and come out feeling your competitive best, ready to beat all the fine competition the contest has to offer you. What usually happens is that the judges will call two or more contestants at a time, choose one who exemplifies a certain quality of a particular body part, and then, dismissing the other or others, call for two more athletes to compare body parts with the one remaining. It is a process of elimination and a test of your emotions. It is also the heart of the competition when you go man-to-man for the overall title.

A common error in the comparison round is to forget that the judges are sitting *below* the athletes, either in some form of orchestra pit or, at very best, in the first row or two of seats, but *lower than the stage.* Some bodybuilders have the idea that leaning backwards during front poses helps make the pose look more heroic. The truth is, however, that when you lean backwards and away from a judge who is seated lower than eye level to begin with, you only afford him a spectacular view of your nostrils and armpits, and muscular nostrils and armpits will add very few points to your score. What makes considerably more sense is to lean *forward* slightly; that will show your best body parts to even greater advantage.

In the final round, at night, you can straighten up and make eye contact with the

The fourth round: posedown with Danny Padilla (left) and Chris Dickerson.

The final round: posing for the audience.

audience. But at every point before that, you must show the judges some personality and considerable respect to go along with your body. Even superhuman bodies still house a human personality inside of them, and the judges will be looking for a demonstration of just that.

It is especially important during this round to show more than the judges want to see. For example, if the judges call you to do a double biceps pose, most athletes think that the judges are only looking at the biceps. Wrong. I want to show them my biceps the best way I can but I will flex every other body part so that the judges see that I built the biceps in proportion to the rest of my body. Proportion is very important and must be demonstrated through your poses.

Preparing for Contest

In amateur contests, the head judge will tell you how much oil, if any, you may use. (There are no restrictions in professional contests.) You shouldn't come out dry, because some of your details will get lost in the bright lights; on the other hand, you shouldn't look shiny. Oil must be rubbed into the skin, not merely left on the surface. I always use a minimum amount of oil, but I sprinkle a few drops of water around just before my entrance for a good glistening level. The lights will certainly make anyone perspire, but it is a good start for me.

Your routine should be well-paced, of

course, with the same interval between poses. If you become confused or make a mistake, do what seasoned actors do: continue as smoothly as you can. Your poise during such an unlikely event will count for a lot.

Regarding your choice of sequence, it's a very smart idea to show the judges and/or the audience your second or third best pose *first,* then your less spectacular poses, then your good ones, and the very best pose last. If you don't feel you have enough good ones in your routine, it's much better to cut down, choose your two best, and do them twice each as long as they are evenly spaced with the rest of your poses.

How do you get pumped up to do your best posing? Assuming weights are not allowed backstage, which is frequently the case, you'll have to become creative. First, determine which body parts *need* to be pumped to look better—not all parts will. If you need a thigh pump, 100 reps or so of squats with no weight are excellent. My favorite weight-less exercises include dips between chairs, push-ups (done with your feet elevated, such as on a chair, and with your fingers facing each other, five inches or so apart), calf raises on steps for each leg, lateral raises with chairs, backhanded isometrics in a doorway, and handstand push-ups. You need to do at least 15 or 20 reps more than you usually do, one set only. When you have finished, go through your entire posing routine hard, 4 or 5 times, to complete your pump. This will also help you become familiar and confident with your routine.

Sportsmanship

Regardless of what happens during a contest, your behavior on stage is being monitored closely by thousands of people as well as the judges, who might come just to see you in the next contest. You must learn how to control your unique disposition on stage, and always appear pleasant regardless of the decision. Above all, do not mumble obscenities while on stage because the judges and the audience can hear or lip-read your remarks. If you are not #1 with the judges, you can still be #1 with the audience. The public is your fan club and without fans there would be no stars.

1981 MR. OLYMPIA

Before the contest, Franco talks with countryman Franco Fassi, publisher of SPORTMAN magazine in Italy.

The tension mounts between rounds.

Franco is announced the winner and his comeback becomes bodybuilding history.

Frequently, place winners have become bigger stars than the overall winners because of the public. If you are disappointed by a decision, create something positive. You have the power to turn any situation around by your thoughts and your attitude. But they have to be positive, not negative.

I certainly did not win every contest that I ever entered, but I have reached and maintained what some would call superstar status. Every bodybuilder has experienced defeat including every top superstar. Throughout the years, I have seen countless temper tantrums both on stage and off. I believe the main reason for these tantrums is the irritability that can be caused by rigid dieting and/or by the use of drugs. My recommendation to combat this is to stop all drugs and return to a normal well-balanced natural diet one week before a contest. It is also a good time to relax and work with your mind.

I know that a very important factor that helped me win the 1981 Mr. Olympia was my mental attitude. All year long, there were rumors about this and claims about that. I was occupied by my chiropractic practice and business concerns—I have a life that is too full to be plagued by rumors and doubts. I also knew that many contestants were worried about me. All they did was train, sit in the sun, and worry about me. Without all that free time to worry, I never doubted the outcome of the contest.

This also relates to your self-confidence. If you are fearful, it shows on stage. Be sure that your presentation radiates self-confidence—no matter what. If you don't win, so what? The only important thing to remember is to always do your best under any circumstances and the best will come back to you.

During that final round, the stage is yours. Impressions do count whether you win or lose, so make yours the best along with your muscular presentation. Afterwards it will be to your advantage to have pictures available and sign autographs for your fans. They will love you.

Chapter 5

BODYBUILDING FOR WOMEN

Advocates for women's bodybuilding have been around for many years. But it has only been recently that bodybuilding for women has really caught on. It is truly amazing how much women have contributed to the sport—especially in the area of competitive posing—in a short time. Women's contests are becoming as popular as the men's contests.

Some women bodybuilders have physiques that are incredibly muscular and well defined. Yet, because of their hormonal differences with men, these women's muscles follow feminine curves and serve only to accent their femininity—they do not look like men, believe me! These hormonal differences (women have more *estrogen* and men have more *testosterone*) mean that women have to train harder than men to become muscular.

Another difference between women and men—besides the obvious—is in body fat content. The average female should have 25 percent body fat, whereas the average male should have about 15 percent body fat. The female structure contains most of its fat in the stomach, hips, and thighs; this is why a woman can't really train successfully with a man's training program. Most women's goals in training will be to reduce the fat in the lower body while building the upper body. Women in general have been tested to be 23 percent weaker in the upper body than in the lower body. Thus weight training is the best way for them to balance and strengthen their bodies.

The first step in becoming a bodybuilder is to trim off all of the fat from the lower body. This is done by high repetition, aerobic-type exercises and through a well-balanced diet.

The lower body most likely should be trained daily whereas the upper body should be trained three times per week with weights. To increase strength and build the upper body, women should use less repetitions and as much weight as they can comfortably handle. To reduce the lower body, they should use very high repetitions with light weight or no weight, and little or no rest between sets.

Once the body is in proportion women can advance to another level of training and begin to zero in on muscularity, definition, and strength. Don't be afraid to do this. Just as there are a lot of myths about male bodybuilders, there are probably double the number for women. The benefits of a healthy diet and vibrant fitness should encourage you to advance and to learn how to sculpt your body into a shape that is pleasing to you.

Before advancing to the training programs, I must say that steroid drugs are even more detrimental to women than they are to men. The female endocrine system is very delicate and is easily put into a state of imbalance. The effects are irreversible and can be devastating.

Note that the weight resistance exercises in the following programs utilize high reps because when women train with heavier weights for less than 20 reps, the effect is an

BEGINNING TRAINING PROGRAM FOR WOMEN

Seated stretch—2 × 25 (166)
Cross flyes—2 × 25 (131)
Incline bench press—2 × 25 (143–4)
Pulldowns—2 × 25 (158–9)
One-arm rowing—2 × 25 (154)
Bent-over lateral raises—2 × 25 (126–6)
Lunges—2 × 25 (151)
Squat (no weight)*—2 × 25 (173)
Calf raises—2 × 25 (170, 177))
Lying side leg raises**—4 × 25 (152)
Bent-leg sit-ups**—4 × 25 (124)
Bent-leg raises**—4 × 25 (124)
Donkey kick**—4 × 25 (135)

*After second week, add 10 lb. dumbbells.
**Do last four exercises daily.

INTERMEDIATE TRAINING PROGRAM FOR WOMEN

Seated stretch—1 × 25 (166)
Cross flyes—2 × 25 (131)
Incline bench press—4 × 25 (143–4)
Pulldowns—4 × 25 (158–9)
T-bar rowing—2 × 25 (181)
One-arm rowing—2 × 25 (154)
Bent-over lateral raises—4 × 25 (125–6)
Lateral raises—3 × 25 (146)
Triceps pushdowns—4 × 25 (182)
Pullover—3 × 20 (161)
Lunges—3 × 25 (151)
Leg extensions—3 × 35 (148)
Leg curls—2 × 35 (147)
Calf raises—4 × 20 (170, 177)
Lying side leg raises—4 × 25 (152)
Bent-leg sit-ups—4 × 25 (124)
Bent-leg raises—4 × 25 (124)
Donkey kicks—4 × 25 (135)

ADVANCED TRAINING PROGRAM FOR WOMEN

Seated stretch—2 × 20 (166)
Incline bench press—4 × 25 (143–4)
Bench press—2 × 25 (123)
Incline flyes—2 × 25
Pulldowns—4 × 25 (158–9)
T-bar rowing—3 × 25 (181)
One-arm rowing—2 × 20 (154)
Bent-over lateral raises—5 × 15 (125–6)
Lateral raises—4 × 15 (146)
Front raises—2 × 15 (139–40)
Triceps pushdowns—4 × 20 (182)
Dumbbell curls—2 × 20 (164–5, 178)
Lying triceps extensions—3 × 20 (153)
Preacher's curl—2 × 20 (156)
Leg extensions—5 × 35 (148)
Leg curls—3 × 35 (147)
Squat—3 × 35 (173)
Calf raises—7 × 20 (170, 177)
Lying side leg raises—4 × 25 (152)
Bent-leg sit-ups—4 × 25 (124)
Bent-leg raises—4 × 25 (124)
Donkey kicks—4 × 25 (135)

Donkey kick, start.

Donkey kick, finish.

Pullover, finish.

Lying side leg raise, start.

Lying side leg raise, finish.

increase in body size. To firm up, get definition, and lose fat, women must train with light weights for 25 reps or more.

This advanced program may be divided into training sessions or can be done at one time three times a week. If you divide it into two days, train the upper body and do the stomach exercises every other day and train the lower body and do the stomach exercises on the other days. Much of what I have written about training intervals and techniques in previous chapters applies to women as well as men. If a woman becomes bored or stale with her present routine, she should change training times, the routine or the order of the routine, or change partners or gyms. She shouldn't quit or get negative. Most of the men's training programs in this book can be modified for women by cutting down on weights and increasing reps. However, the programs just outlined are the most beneficial for a woman's physical structure.

Chapter 6

BODYBUILDING FOR OTHER SPORTS

Weight training and bodybuilding can lead you to some striking improvements in the sport of your choice. Resistance exercises are used now for every sport, especially at championship levels. When training for a particular sport there are two aspects to the training. One aspect is to train for skills used in the sport and the other is to add exercises using weights. Weight training will increase strength, stamina, endurance, and also will balance the musculature. In each sport, certain muscles are overused while other muscles are not used at all. This creates a muscular imbalance within an athlete's structure and should be corrected with the proper weight training program. Weight training also improves coordination, which is of utmost importance in any sport.

After a satisfying boxing career, Franco next went on to win powerlifting championships.

Football

Many running backs have tremendous upper-body strength and many linemen have astonishing quickness. Walter Payton of the Chicago Bears, a true superstar, is not huge as football players go, but he can press 300 lbs. and bench-press 400+ lbs. with no problem. Cullen Bryant of the Los Angeles Rams can bench-press more than that; his hand and arm strength is such that he almost never fumbles. I'm not saying these men owe *everything* to weight training; after all, they are remarkable athletes with many gifts.

I'm going to list the weight exercises that, generally, are most beneficial to football players, and suggest that you make your own selections of which ones to emphasize, based on your personal goals. If you're a lineman, for instance, I would suggest considerably more emphasis on the squat, bench press, and deadlift because you're after raw size and power, and those are the powerlifting exercises. As a running back, you would want to do a wide variety of leg exercises. Whatever your position, you should determine your own needs within this program, simply through common sense.

FOOTBALL

Stretching—20 reps each of the leg stretch, side bends (20 to each side), and calf stretch. (121, 168, 126)
Calf raises—5 × 15, with maximum weight. This exercise will strengthen your acceleration out of your stance. (170, 177)
Squat—3 × 15. It is important to do the full squat. (173)
Front squat—3 × 15. (141)
Straight-leg dead lift—3 × 10. Note that you can't use maximum weight here as you can in the bent-leg version. (180)
Leg extensions—4 × 25. This is the best exercise to strengthen and protect the knees. (148)
Leg curls—2 × 25. (147)
Bench press—3 × 15. (123)
Incline bench press—2 × 15. (143–4)
Barbell rowing—3 × 15. (122)
Pulldowns—3 × 15. (158–9)
Pullovers—2 × 15. This is an excellent exercise for the rib cage. (161)
Bent-over lateral raises—4 × 10. (125–6)
Lateral raises—4 × 10. (146)
Triceps pushdowns—5 × 10. I emphasize doing 5 sets because it's critical to all legal use of the hands in football. (182)
Wrist curls—2 × 15. (186)
Sit-ups—4 × 25. You can alternate these with the next exercise for some variety, if you choose. (171)
Leg raises—4 × 25. (150)
Repeat the stretching exercises.

Basketball

It's taken basketball longer than most other sports to recognize the value of weight training. With the sport's emphasis on quickness, basketball players have traditionally subscribed to the "musclebound" myth about bodybuilding and stayed away. But today, weight programs are being utilized for individuals, and even whole teams, at high school, college, and pro levels.

Basketball players usually have long muscles and need weight training to strengthen them. Players whose rebounding abilities are important to their teams have trained successfully to build their gripping power and gain some welcome muscular weight to throw around under the boards. Smaller players have used weight training to add to their agility, quickness, and aggressiveness. And almost everybody can increase their leaping abilities through sensible weight training.

Basketball training can be done before or after weight training. On the days you compete, however, it is not advisable to weight train.

BASKETBALL

Stretching—25 reps each of the hamstring stretch, calf stretch, and side bends. (121, 126, 168)
Tricep pushdowns—4 × 15. (182)
Incline bench press—3 × 15. (143–4)
Pulldowns—3 × 15. (158–9)
Bent-over lateral raises—3 × 15. (125–6)
Leg extensions—3 × 20. (148)
Calf raises—4 × 20. (170, 177)
Jump squat—2 × 10. (145)
Sit-ups—3 × 25. (171)
Leg raises—3 × 25. (150)
Jump rope—Up to 10 minutes. Still one of the greatest exercises on earth for legs, footwork, agility, hand/eye coordination, stamina, and wind. (145)
Speed running—Up to 2 miles. For basketball, running 2 miles is much better than jogging 4.

Baseball

Many baseball players come to our chiropractic center. Using muscle testing techniques, I usually find muscular imbalances which come from overstressing one side of the body, particularly in pitching. Weight training can be very useful in preventing and correcting these muscular imbalances.

According to one of its most durable clichés, baseball is a game of inches, so again you have to be careful about exercises which threaten your quickness. Weight training can enhance your throwing abilities to some degree. The shoulder and triceps exercises listed here will help if you are an outfielder or pitcher, but be sure to do as much ball-throwing as you normally do.

Batting is where weight training can help you the most. You should train to help the muscles which put the snap and rotation moves into a smooth, level swing, and that's what we'll do.

BASEBALL

Cross flyes—2 × 15. (131)
Bent-over lateral raises—3 × 15. (125–6)
Lateral raises—3 × 15. (146)
Triceps pushdowns—3 × 15. (182)
Wrist curls—3 × 15. (186)
Leg extensions—3 × 15. (148)
Calf raises—3 × 25. (170, 177)
Sit-ups—3 × 25. (171)
Leg raises—3 × 25. (150)
Leg stretching—2 × 20. (121, 166)
Side bends—2 × 20. (168)
Speed running—2–3 miles.

Soccer

The emphasis here is on the legs. However, I am including three exercises for triceps and shoulders which should be of primary interest to goal tenders, for added gripping and throwing strength. Train as fast as you can; soccer is a game of endurance and stamina, and your workouts can help with that.

SOCCER

Leg extensions—5 × 30. (148)
Calf raises—5 × 25. (170, 177)
Front calf raises—5 × 25. (139–40)
Lunges—4 × 25. (151)
Leg stretching—2 × 20. (121, 166)
Calf stretching—2 × 20. (126)
Triceps pushdowns—2 × 15. (182)
Lateral raises—2 × 15. (146)
Bent-over lateral raises—2 × 15. (125–6)
Jumping rope—Up to 10 minutes. (145)
Side bends—4 × 25. (168)
Hyperextension—4 × 25. An excellent toner for the lower back. (142)
Sit-ups—4 × 25. (171)

Boxing and Karate

It was boxing that introduced me to weights in the first place. I shadowboxed a few rounds daily, holding a pair of 2½-pound dumbbells, to strengthen my punch with either hand and to increase my ability to carry my fists high through a long bout. I honestly believe the weights helped me become the lightweight champion of Italy and increased my number of knockouts.

Karate employs much of the same footwork, moves, and muscles that boxing does; the blows are simply delivered differently, to different targets, and delivered with the feet as well. This program can help build your endurance and power for either sport.

BOXING

Seated leg stretching—2 × 25. (166)
Side bends—2 × 25. (168)
Bent-over lateral raises—2 × 25. (125–6)
Triceps pushdowns—4 × 25. (182)
Leg extensions—3 × 25. (148)
Calf raises—3 × 25. (170, 177)
Calf stretching—2 × 10. (126)
Hamstring stretching—2 × 10. (142)
Weight boxing—Three 3-minute rounds, with 2–5 lb. dumbbells or plates. (186)
Jumping rope—Three to five 3-minute rounds. (145)

Hockey

As with soccer, fully half of a sound weight training program for hockey should emphasize the legs. But this time there is a puck to be handled and shot with a stick. The following is an excellent hockey training program.

HOCKEY

Squat—3 × 25. (173)
Leg press—3 × 20. (149)
Leg extensions—4 × 25. (148)
Leg curls—2 × 25. (147)
Calf raises—4 × 20. (170, 177)
Front calf raises—4 × 20. (139–40)
Wrist curls—4 × 20. (186)
Barbell rowing—3 × 15. (122)
Lateral raises—3 × 15. (146)
Leg stretching—2 × 20. (121, 166)
Side bends—2 × 20. (168)
Sit-ups—2 × 20. (171)

Running

In training for running, you should train the upper body first, to get some extra blood up there as early as you can. The blood will go to the legs once you actually begin running.

Why train the upper body at all when the legs do all the work? I know at least three reasons: 1) failure to do so will make your legs even more disproportionately strong than they already are; 2) upper body development will help you resist the tension which occurs naturally in running; and 3) more powerful arm thrusts will actually help you stride better.

RUNNING

Bench press—3 × 20. (123)
Barbell rowing—2 × 20. (122)
Pulldowns—2 × 20. (158–9)
Bent-over lateral raises—3 × 10. (125–6)
Lateral raises—3 × 10. (146)
Triceps pushdowns—4 × 10. (182)
Dumbbell curls—2 × 10. (164–5, 178)
Forearm curls—2 × 15. (186)
Leg extensions—4 × 50. (148)
Lunges—4 × 40. (151)
Squat—3 × 25. (173)
Calf raises—5 × 40. (170, 177)
Front calf raises—5 × 40. (139–40)
Abdominal training—Sit-ups, leg raises, and side bends, 2 × 50 each, in rotation. (171, 150, 168)
Stretching—calf and leg stretch, 2 × 10 each, in rotation. (126, 121, 166)

Amateur and Professional Wrestling

In wrestling, you need to train for all the bulk and power you can use. The following routine includes all three powerlifting exercises, and I further suggest that you perform every exercise listed here with maximum weight. Bruno San Martino trains with very heavy weights and is extremely strong. Weight training has been a definite asset to his wrestling.

WRESTLING

Squat—4 × 10. (173)
Leg press—4 × 10. (149)
Dead lift—4 sets, up to 5 reps. (133)
Bench press—4 × 10. (123)
Barbell rowing—4 × 10. (122)
Triceps pushdowns—5 × 10. (182)
Barbell curls—4 × 8. (174-5)
Standing press—3 × 10. (176, 179)
Presses behind neck—3 × 10. (157)
Lateral raises—4 × 10. (146)
Wrist curls—4 × 10. (186)

Tennis and Other Racquet Sports

Probably the first prominent tennis player to use weights to good advantage was Australia's Frank Sedgman, back in the early 1950s. Even though Sedgman was quite dominant in his era, he didn't exactly spawn legions of imitators when it came to using weights. Tennis players today generally come to bodybuilding for remedial purposes, such as rebuilding a knee. There isn't a lot of muscle among today's top players but their legs are usually hard and well-shaped.

Two exercises, which are frequently overlooked yet important to tennis, are the leg extension and reversed forearm curls. The former is the best single tennis exercise; not only does it add strength to your hitting foundation, but it helps you plant your weight more solidly prior to your stroke. Best of all, it helps prevent knee injuries. Forearm curls will strengthen your grip, add power to your stroke (off either side), and will help you prevent tennis elbow.

TENNIS

Lunges—2 × 20. (151)
Leg extensions—4 × 25. (148)
Calf raises—2 × 20. (170, 177)
Front calf raises—2 × 20. (139-40)
Barbell rowing—2 × 10. (122)
One-arm rowing—2 × 10. (154)
Bent-over lateral raises—2 × 10. (125-6)
Lateral raises—2 × 10. (146)
Triceps pushdowns—2 × 10. (182)
Wrist curls—2 × 10. (186)
Abdomen—Sit-ups and leg raises, 4 × 25 each, in rotation. (171, 150)
Stretching—5 reps each of leg stretching, calf stretching, and side bends. (121, 126, 168)

Skiing

Weight training, quite honestly, cannot do a great deal for your sense of balance or your skiing reflexes. Still, it is quite possible to train with weights sensibly for skiing, because better-developed muscles make better shock absorbers. The emphasis of this routine is on the legs, of course, but those exercises for increasing upper-body strength will help you push off better. This is very important for those who wish to cross-country ski. And, since you might as well face the possibility that you will fall—somehow, someday—you'll be a lot better off falling with a well-muscled body than a frail one.

SKIING

Lunges—3 × 25. (151)
Squat—4 × 25. (173)
Leg extensions—4 × 25. (148)
Leg curls—1 × 25. (147)
Calf raises—4 × 25. (170, 177)
Front calf raises—4 × 25. (139–40)
Bench press—3 × 20. (123)
Pulldowns—3 × 20. (158–9)
Chins in front of neck—3 × 10. (127)
Lateral raises—3 × 10. (146)
Triceps pushdowns—3 × 10. (182)
Wrist curls—3 × 10. (186)
Abdominals—Sit-ups, leg raises, and side bends, 4 × 25 each, in rotation. (171, 150, 168)
Stretching—Leg stretch and calf stretch, 2 × 25 each, in rotation. (121, 126)

Weightlifting

It is very important to maintain both speed and strength during weightlifting training. Each individual is different; however, the body has to be kept limber. Training emphasis here is placed more on the extensor muscles. You should train three to four times per week. After each training session, hang for a few minutes from a chinning bar to decompress the spine.

WEIGHTLIFTING

Snatch—7 × 2. (172)
Clean and jerk—7 × 2. (128–9)
Clean—5 × 3. (128)
Standing press* (176)
  Front—3 × 5.
  Behind the neck—3 × 5.
Barbell rowing—3 × 5. (122)
Lateral raises—3 × 5. (146)
Triceps pushdowns—5 × 10. (182)
Squat (7 sets—add weight with each set)—
  2 × 8, 2 × 6, 1 × 4, 1 × 2, 1 × 1. (173)
Leg press—5 × 5. (149)
Leg extensions—5 × 10. (148)
Leg curls—3 × 10. (147)
Calf raises—5 × 10. (170, 177)
Bent-leg sit-ups—3 × 20. (124)
Leg stretch—2 × 10. (121, 166)
Standing side bends—2 × 10. (180)

*Alternate between front and back.

Powerlifting

I have observed that the majority of powerlifters and weightlifters are overweight. This is not necessary, because being fat does not increase one's strength. Strength and concentration are of prime concern in powerlifting. The following program has been designed for increasing both strength and total fitness. Please note that the weight increases with every set on the bench press, squat, and deadlift. Also remember that the body usually takes longer to recuperate between workouts in powerlifting because of the heavy poundages needed for training.

After each training session hang for a few minutes from the chinning bar to decompress the spine.

POWERLIFTING

Deadlift (increase weight)—2 × 7, 2 × 5,
  2 × 4, 2 × 2, 2 × 1. (133)
Bench press (increase weight)—2 × 7, 2 × 5,
  2 × 4, 2 × 2, 2 × 1. (123)
Incline bench press—3 × 7. (143)
Flyes—3 × 7. (137)
Barbell rowing—4 × 7. (122)
Squat—2 × 7, 2 × 5, 2 × 4, 2 × 2, 2 × 1. (173)
Leg press—4 × 7. (149)
Leg extension—4 × 15. (148)
Calf raises—5 × 15. (170, 177)
Bent-leg sit-ups—2 × 20. (124)
Leg stretch—2 × 10. (121)
Side bends—2 × 10. (168)

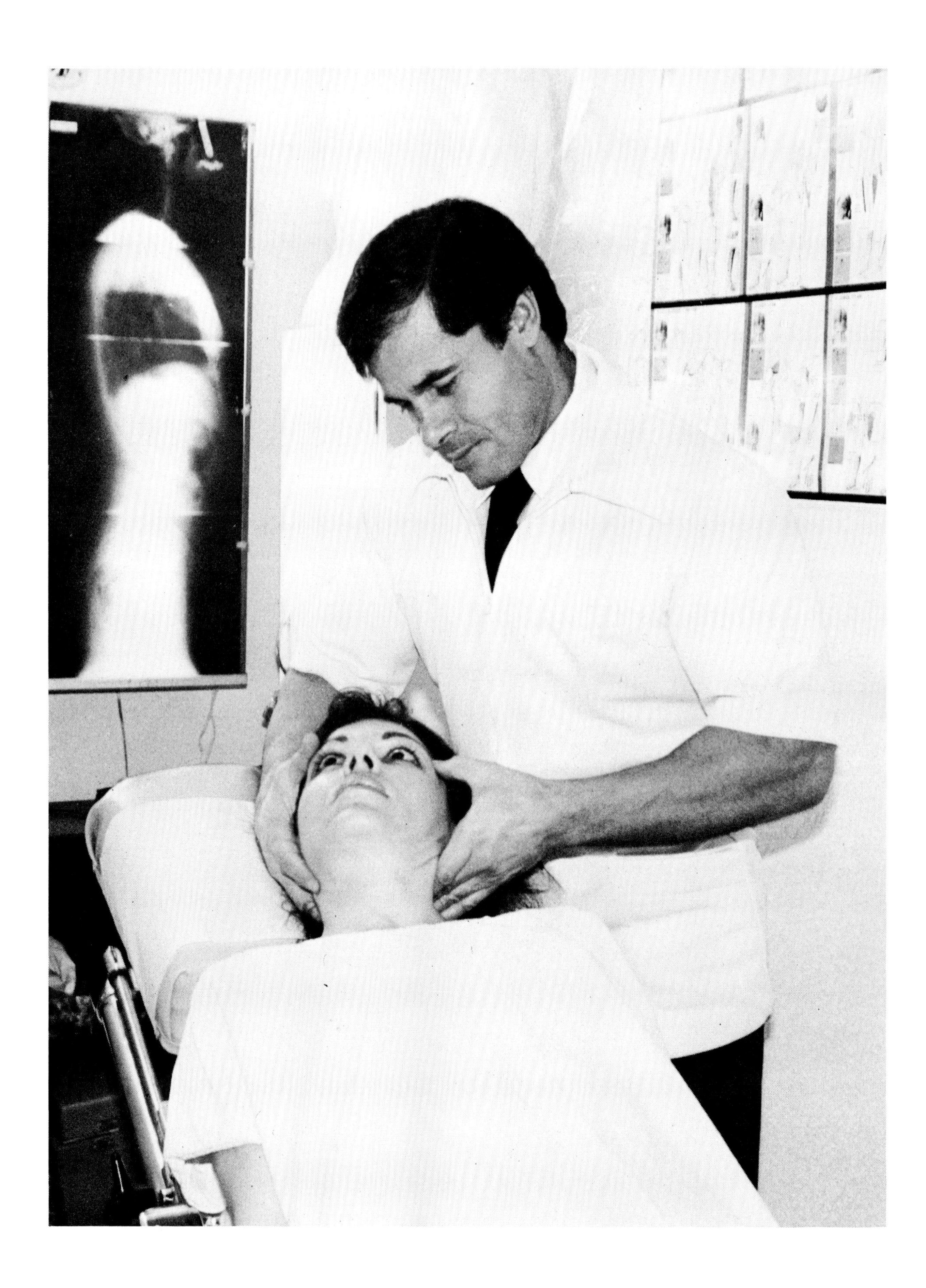

Chapter 7

SPORTS INJURIES—PREVENTION AND TREATMENT

More and more doctors are taking a holistic approach to health, accepting as fact that the body, mind, and spirit work together. To achieve your goals, you must work in all three areas. Because the body, to a great extent, is controlled by the mind, each of us has the power to create whatever it is that we want out of life including a champion body. A healthy body at its best incorporates a healthy, positive mental attitude.

There are hundreds of excellent bodybuilders who have not achieved champion status because their mental forces are scattered and their main focus of attention is on something else, such as what might happen if they don't win at contest. I believe that concentration is the key to bodybuilding success. And such concentration applies to avoiding injuries as well as reaching your personal goals.

The body is controlled by the brain and spinal cord. From the spinal cord branch 31 pairs of spinal nerves that send nerve messages to all parts of the body. If there is an interference with the transmission of nerve messages to a particular muscle or body part, you are more susceptible to injuries because there will be a corresponding weakness in that area.

The most common injuries come from the muscles being strained and the ligaments being sprained. When this occurs, the vertebrae of the spine are moved out of position and a slight displacement of the bones takes place. These phenomena also can involve the extremities. The common term for this is "pinched nerve," which means there is pressure on a particular nerve or group of nerves and the nerve supply from the brain and spinal cord to the organ or extremity is diminished.

In our chiropractic center, we have found pinched nerves to be especially common with powerlifters and bodybuilders. Heavy lifting, particularly squats, causes compression in the lower back. In many instances this compression results in problems with the legs such as *sciatica* or muscle weakness. Sometimes the legs even diminish in size; the muscles actually can atrophy. When the normal nerve function is restored, the symptoms usually become reversible and the body returns to normal. Sometimes certain exercises have to be eliminated, however, or the problem will continue because of the constant aggravation and stress on the weakened body part.

Another important aspect in injuries is blood circulation. Exercising keeps the blood circulating throughout the body, so the tissues and cells get the proper supply of nutrients. For example, the brain depends on the oxygen and carbohydrates carried in the blood for fuel. If either is lacking, brain functions are impaired. Exercise also slows down degeneration of cells because exercise forces you to do deep breathing. Think of your brain as a power plant that needs fuel. This is a good reason why high protein diets without carbohydrates should not be recommended.

Without glucose, the brain cannot function properly. The usual symptoms of a lack of glucose are irritability, fatigue, dizziness, and lack of concentration. Each of these symptoms can make a person more susceptible to injuries, particularly due to lack of concentration. When you go to the gym to train, concentrate on your training. If you go to socialize, then do so after training. You simply cannot concentrate on muscle growth and talking at the same time.

Causes of Injuries

The most common causes of injuries are: poor mental concentration; protein deficiencies; lack of proper nutrients, especially vitamins and minerals; overtraining and/or incorrect training; lack of stretching; and not warming up. Regardless of what you are doing, mental concentration is the key to success. Whatever you do, the results are realized in direct proportion to the amount of concentrated effort you exert. If you are trying to concentrate on two things at the same time, such as working out and talking, you are not putting all of your energy into your training. To progress and move on to heavier weights and a more advanced workout, you have to put all of your energy into your form, style, sets, and reps. As soon as your mind wanders and you pick up a heavier weight and begin training without full concentration, you are setting up an injury.

Whenever your training program becomes too routine, the challenge is lost and it is time to revise the program or move onward to a more advanced program. By avoiding routinized training, you can sharpen your concentration, which is the key to successful bodybuilding.

The Need for Protein

During training, muscle fibers are microscopically broken down or torn. The body must then repair the torn tissue and does so by using amino acids as building blocks. This is one of the reasons why protein is valuable in your training diet. Lack of sufficient protein produces a slow rate of repair. If this happens, then you will not progress with your training. It is also important to rest between heavy training sessions because, during the resting phase, regeneration is taking place, provided there is a sufficient amount of protein to complete the repairs.

If minerals are lacking, the bones can become more brittle and the muscles and ligaments that attach to the bones can easily become separated. Minerals—particularly calcium and magnesium—are also needed for muscle movements. If calcium is lacking, the muscle will begin to contract and spasm. Vitamins and minerals are important; however,

vitamins do not work without minerals and for muscles and bones, the minerals are of prime importance. Heavy training and a high protein diet will increase your body's requirements for calcium, magnesium, and potassium.

Overtraining and Incorrect Training

There is a fine line between adequate training and overtraining. Most everyone who comes to me for professional advice about a training program, has been overtraining. When this happens the body is more susceptible to injury. You cannot make gains if you overtrain. The most common signs of overtraining are: lack of a pump, fatigue, lowered resistance to infections or colds, lack of concentration, more than the usual aches and pains from training, less desire for training, and lack of motivation.

Incorrect training causes an imbalance in the body. This is why I recommend that you follow the training programs in the sequences given. Some muscle groups have to be trained more and some less, otherwise the entire structure is thrown out of balance and a weakness in certain areas of the body is created that can easily set up an injury.

Proper exercise form is another factor that will help you avoid injury. Look at yourself while you are training and be sure that your movements are smooth and flowing. Or have someone watch you exercise and check your form against the form shown in the Exercise Glossary. If your movements are jerky or if you throw your body around in completing a movement, you are injuring yourself.

Weight training causes the muscles to become more contracted. This exercise, combined with normal daily activities, contributes to muscle spasms. Therefore, before and after training, the muscles need to be stretched. The Dallas Cowboys have reduced their injury rate by 23 percent by adding stretching exercises to their training programs. Every patient that comes to the office for chiropractic care is given some corrective exercises to do; usually these exercises are designed to stretch and strengthen the muscles.

The most common problems with weight trained athletes are compression in the spine and tight hamstring muscles. To reduce spinal compression, I always recommend hanging from a chinning bar for a few minutes after each training session. Depending on your training program, you might also hang from the bar for a few minutes during training. Tight hamstring muscles contribute to lower back pain, so the hamstring muscles must be stretched daily.

Warming up, like stretching, is one of the best ways to prevent injuries. Synovial fluid acts as a lubricant for the joints and must be circulating around the joints prior to heavy training. Before training every body part, do each exercise with light weights for at least 20 repetitions.

In cooler weather it is important to warm up longer. I also recommend warming down after a training session. Take a few minutes and hang from a chinning bar and/or do some slow stretching so the body will begin to slow down prior to leaving the gym and rushing elsewhere.

Injury Prevention

You can do a great deal to prevent problems, but you should not try to be your own physician or trainer. Anytime there is a group of people together in a gym, many new ideas are marketed. Some are excellent and some are not—you have to remember that each body is different and just because something works for your friend, it does not mean it will work for you. It may actually do you harm. If you feel uncomfortable on a certain piece of equipment, then don't use it.

Gyms are full of people who have no background in body mechanics—or anything else, for that matter—who are constantly telling everybody what to do. Instead of listening to them, tune in to your own body and learn to distinguish what makes you feel better. Never force yourself to do something just because everybody else is doing it. You could cause a problem. If you are unsure as to what you should do, always seek professional advice. You could save yourself years of needless pain.

Before I go on to discuss injury prevention by body part and injury, I should add some qualifications regarding the "professional advice" you seek in regard to sports injuries. Your family doctor may be excellent for treating illnesses, but his knowledge about sports injuries may be limited. The worst thing you can do is let him or her prescribe a painkiller and advise you to take it easy for a while. I am in favor of your seeing a Doctor of Chiropractic for certain sports injuries, not because I'm interested in having you as a client, but because of the training I know such doctors have. The majority of their studies center around body mechanics (kinesiology) and nutrition, the two areas of medicine that most often play major roles in sports injuries. Chiropractors can help relieve nerve compression that naturally occurs when lifting heavy weights.

Having said that, let's look at injury prevention.

Ankle. The most common cause of ankle injuries is having the ankle stiff and the calf

muscles too tight during strenuous activity. The best way of preventing ankle injury is to stand with the ball of your foot on a block or on stairs and let the heels drop down off of the block or stairs. This is excellent for women. They usually have shorter calf muscles due to wearing high-heeled shoes.

Knee. The knee is one of the most complicated articulations of the body. The only natural movement for the knee is bending forward. Thus, squatting with your feet too far apart or with your toes pointed in or out too much can easily contribute to knee problems. Tight hamstring muscles is another contributing factor to knee problems, so stretching the hamstring muscles daily cannot be overemphasized. If you do injure your knee, it should be checked by a physician since knee injuries can easily progress into something serious.

Femur. The femur joint is usually very stable. However, squatting with the toes pointed in or out too much, or doing a split-type exercise to stretch the inner thigh muscles can cause femur problems. I do not recommend stretching the inner thigh muscles and believe that this should be avoided. This type of injury should be treated by a Doctor of Chiropractic because if the femur is slightly displaced, there is no other effective treatment except an adjustment with kinesiology. Only in this way can the muscles around the femur be strengthened.

Lower back. Approximately 90 million Americans suffer from lower back problems. In bodybuilding, the lower back problems are usually caused by straight leg sit-ups, roman chair sit-ups, squats, deadlifts, presses, and sleeping on your stomach. I designed the training programs in this book to avoid the above problems; however, I must emphasize using correct form while training, and refraining from any jerking movements.

The most important exercise for bodybuilders who have sustained a lower back injury is to stretch the hamstring muscles (see page 121). Another exercise would be standing side bends; lying on your back and pulling one knee to your chest, then the other, or bending your knees and rocking back and forth on the floor while holding them with your arms, also are effective exercises.

If you have sustained a lower back injury avoid all press exercises, sit-ups, squats, and deadlifts until complete recovery has taken place. Consult a Doctor of Chiropractic to determine when you should continue.

Middle Back. The middle back is easily affected by presses and T-bar rowing, because the ribs, which attach to the vertebral bodies, are stressed during these exercises. In many instances, the ribs are moved slightly out of position and the result can be a stabbing pain, particularly when you move in a certain direction, cough, or sneeze. One-arm rowing sometimes helps this area; however, the most effective treatment is chiropractic care.

Neck. Neck problems are common in bodybuilding because of some form of muscular imbalance. Usually the trapezius muscles are too strong and the anterior neck muscles are weak. Neck problems can be aggravated by presses and by holding the hands behind the neck while doing sit-ups. These exercises should be eliminated from your workout until the symptoms subside. When doing sit-ups, place your hands on your chest and you will exercise the anterior neck flexors by moving your head up and down.

Shoulder. The shoulder is the only joint in the body that is supported by muscles. I have emphasized bent-over lateral raises, because it is one of the best for preventing shoulder injuries. The most common exercise for causing shoulder injuries is the reverse curl and should be eliminated from your workouts along with presses until a shoulder injury has healed.

Elbows. The most common cause of elbow problems in bodybuilding is an imbalance between the biceps and the triceps muscles. Usually the biceps are stronger than the triceps. The triceps are long muscles and must be worked harder so that they are stronger than the biceps muscles. This tendency to underwork the triceps is why I have recommended more sets for them than for the biceps. If you

should need to work harder to develop your biceps, be certain to increase your work on the triceps to keep them in balance.

Wrist. Wrist problems are usually due to an imbalance in the forearm muscles or to flexing the hand too far back toward the elbow. Hanging wrist curls will assist in balancing the muscles and correcting the causes of wrist injuries.

Muscle soreness. Muscle soreness is caused by training and usually begins the day after training and lasts for approximately 3-5 days. If it persists or is severe, this usually indicates a deficiency of Vitamin C.

Muscle Spasm. Spasm is a term applied to involuntary contractions of muscles. Spasms can last for several days. Nerve pressure and lack of circulation also contribute to this problem. Common remedies usually include applying ice or moist heat on the troubled area; increasing intake of minerals, especially calcium; and stretching muscles surrounding the affected area.

Muscle Cramp. A muscle cramp is a contraction that usually comes and goes rapidly. It is usually caused by nerve pressure and/or a calcium, magnesium, and potassium deficiency.

Sprain. A sprain is a ligament injury. It can be caused by overstretching the ligaments while under stress or by too much twisting in areas around the joints that cause a partial tearing of the fibers. A sprain is one of the few problems that requires you to stop training the area of the sprain. Should you continue training the injured area, you will aggravate the injury and cause complications. You must see a doctor and rest the injured area.

Strain. A strain is a muscle tendon injury and is one of the most common injuries for athletes. The most common area for a strain is where the tendon attaches to the bone, such as the area of the anterior shoulder where the biceps tendon attaches. This injury is more common in bodybuilders who take steroid drugs and thyroid medication because of the mineral imbalances that these drugs create.

Bursitis. This is an inflammation of the bursa in the joint. A bursa is a saclike cavity containing synovial fluids to protect the joints from rubbing together. Each joint contains multiple bursae (8 in each shoulder and 5 in each knee), and isolation of the particular bursa that is inflamed has to be done by a skilled practitioner. Such joint problems can be greatly aggravated by training on machines that restrict the normal movement of the joint. This is another reason why it is better to use free style weights.

When you have this type of problem, consuming citrus fruits during training should be avoided because citric acid neutralizes the synovial fluid in the joints. If you suspect you have a problem with the bursa, most experts recommend that you not use heat. Heat increases inflammation of the fluid and the joint. I do not recommend having the fluid drained, except in severe cases, because the body will only produce more fluid to replace what has been drained. Ice probably is the best treatment to reduce the inflammation, along with elevation of the injured area.

Hernia. A hernia is a protrusion of an organ or a part through connective tissue or through a wall of the cavity in which it is normally enclosed. It comes as a result from a weakening of its supporting structures. In weight training, the most common type is the inguinal hernia in the groin, which occurs when intra-abdominal structures descend through the inguinal canal. If you have a hernia, you should seek professional medical care because lifting weights will aggravate it.

Tendonitis. Tendonitis is the inflammation of a tendon, which usually results from overuse of a particular area, or sometimes from a lack of circulation in the area. I have found that one of the best treatments for tendonitis is to apply ice to the inflamed area for one minute, then moist heat for 7 minutes twice a day. This is another injury where the area should not be trained until fully healed.

Fractures. A fracture is a break in the continuity of bone. There are many types of fractures and some are more severe than others. If you have reason to suspect that you have fractured some part of your body, then by all means see a doctor immediately. You will need to be examined and x-rayed. Do not attempt to treat fractures yourself. I have found minerals valuable in speeding up the healing time of fractures.

Exercises That Should Not Be Done

Throughout this book, I have attempted to make you aware of the fact that no matter what happens to the body, it tries to maintain balance and equilibrium. This tendency (homeostasis) applies to the body's structure as well as its organs. The body always tries to keep going and to function as normally as possible in every situation. Thus, as soon as an imbalance is created in the body, it is immediately more susceptible to various injuries.

Because I have seen several exercises done repeatedly that actually cause imbalances in the structure, I have listed the most common ones below. Believe me, they are of no benefit to your body.

- Jumping jacks
- Twisting the spine, particularly with a stick on the shoulders
- Bench squat
- Head stand
- Side bends with weights
- Roman chair sit-ups
- Wide-grip bench press or incline press

Antigravity equipment. Antigravity apparatus (boots that allow you to hang upside down from a bar) has become more popular in recent years and the idea is excellent, especially for people with irregularities in the spine. Gravity pulls us down and contributes to compression in joints and also in organs. We have been familiar with antigravity machines for several years, and have used and recommended them for many of our patients. However, we have also found conditions where the antigravity machines were contraindicated and actually contributed to problems. I recommend checking with your doctor before using them.

Treatment of Injuries

Most injuries require professional care and should be seen by a doctor who specializes in sports injuries and understands the mechanism of various exercises. Many times you will be able to continue training, but your program will have to be revised. As I mentioned earlier, Doctors of Chiropractic are excellent with sports injuries that do not require surgery, because they are experts in structural alignment, body mechanics, and corrective exercises. Most of them are very well-versed in nutrition, also.

Listed below are some guidelines that are recommended for home treatment of sports injuries.

- Apply ice immediately after the injury has occurred.
- Try to relax the muscles by applying pressure at the center of the spasm.
- Use moist heat on chronic muscle spasms.
- Do stretching exercises.
- If you are injured while training and the pain is severe, send for professional help immediately.

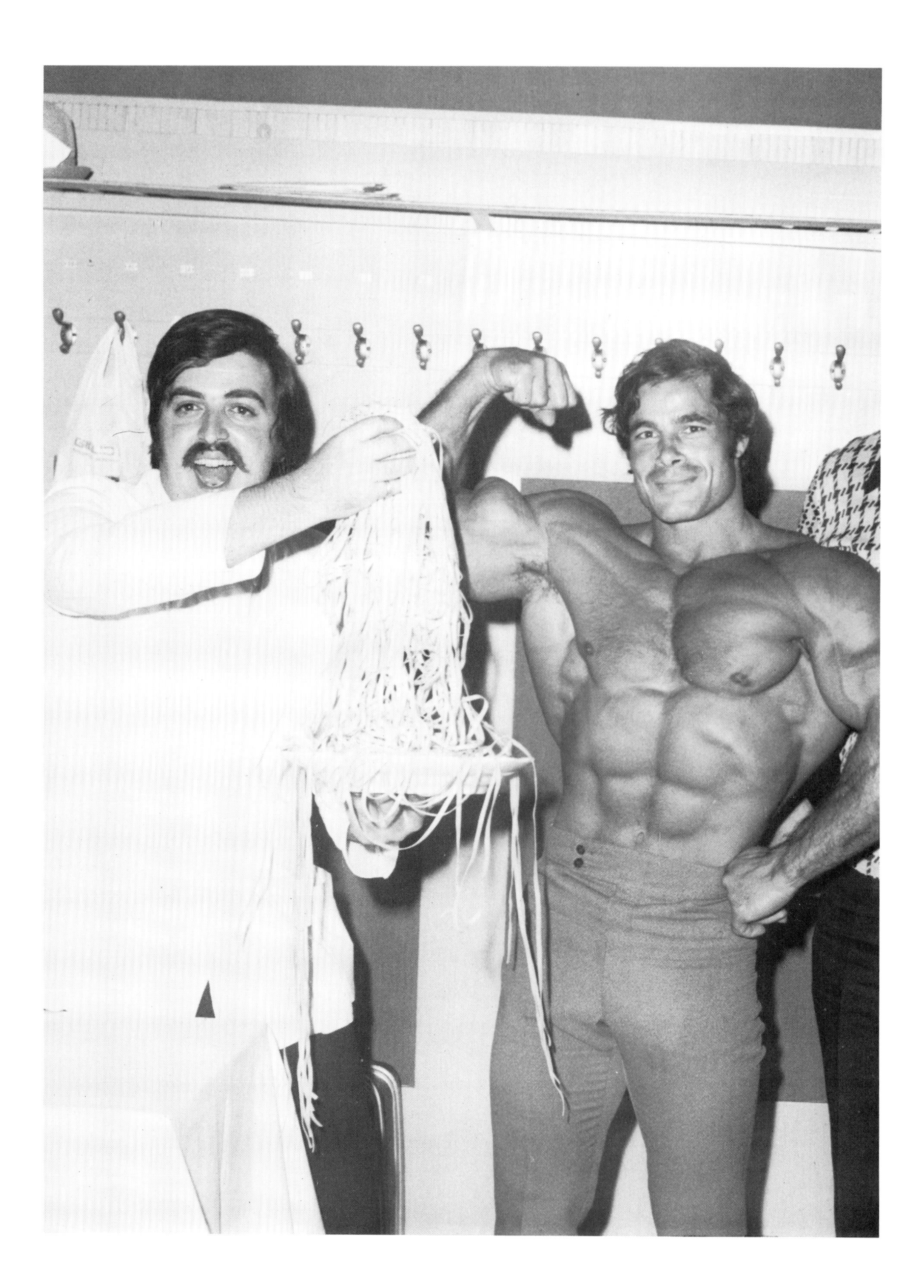

Chapter 8

NUTRITION

As you become more involved in bodybuilding training, you will need to learn how to increase your food supplements and to change your eating habits. Vigorous training sets up a stress condition in the body that requires strict attention to the foods you eat so essential nutrients are replaced more frequently than is necessary for the average person. I will provide you with informal guidelines for using a variety of nutrients as well as provide suggestions on how to improve your eating habits.

Food Combining: The Right Way to Eat

Before I explain the basics of nutrition, I would like to tell you some things about the importance of proper eating habits and the preparation of food. Knowing what vitamins and minerals can do for you is important, but if you don't eat foods in a proper order or if you prepare food in such a way that you destroy the food's nutrient values, all that valuable knowledge will be wasted.

My Background in Nutrition

As you know, I come from the remote island of Sardinia, which is located in the Mediterranean Sea between France, Italy, and Spain. The people of my hometown still use the same cooking methods that they have used for hundreds of years. I was fortunate enough to spend the first 19 years of my life there, eating only fresh, organically grown food.

Sardinians naturally eat well because they

rarely purchase anything from a store. They have their own animals and grow their own food without any sprays, chemicals, or hormones. Fruits and vegetables are always eaten in season, when they are picked fresh and can be cooked or eaten raw—without processing. Because there is little in the way of refrigeration on such a poor island, meat and poultry also are eaten fresh. And when the meat is cooked, it is roasted in the fireplace over a wood fire where it is watched and turned constantly. Thus, the meat cooks evenly by the heat and very little of the smoke gets into it.

It is customary in Europe as well as Sardinia to eat food in the following order. First, we have a small bowl of soup, which would cue the body's digestive system to prepare for digestion. Second, we would have the main course of dinner, which would provide protein (fish, poultry, or meat). Afterward, we ate our salad. Later, we might have a small amount of fresh fruit—I cannot remember my mother ever opening a can of anything—and cheese. These would provide us with carbohydrates. We drank wine with our meals, which aided digestion and provided a few minerals.

By eating protein foods first, the digestive juices were not diluted and the most difficult-to-digest nutrients had the best chance to be fully digested and assimilated by the body. Imagine my surprise when studying for my Ph.D. in nutrition that my people, though poor and barely educated (at least compared to most Americans), knew more about eating correctly than most Americans! When I arrived in America, I noticed that almost everyone was eating huge plates of salad and slices of bread first. I tried this and found myself feeling very bloated and uncomfortable. Then I learned that most Americans are always on some kind of diet and that, by eating the salad and bread first, they think that they will fill up and not eat as much of the more fattening foods. Actually, they end up eating more and digesting it less.

Other Examples of Poor Eating Habits

I was very surprised to see people grilling meat with charcoal in the United States. When meat is grilled with charcoal, the poisons from the coal and smoke accumulate in the meat. Studies have shown these poisons to be carcinogenic; in fact, one charbroiled steak is equal to smoking over 100 cigarettes. I avoid eating anything that has been cooked this way and recommend that you do likewise.

Another thing that amazes me is the number of people who, in trying to reduce their weight, drink diet drinks. These drinks are loaded with all types of chemicals (including sodium chloride, which causes water retention). These chemicals have been known to place a strain on the thyroid gland, altering its regulation of the metabolic rate. Such an alteration actually causes weight reduction to be more difficult! Along with the fluid retention caused by the sodium chloride found in most diet drinks, reduced metabolism is not going to help one lose weight. This is just another example of how "dieting" to lose weight is self-defeating.

To me, the answer to dieting is simple: All things in moderation—protein, fat, and unrefined carbohydrates. Eat small amounts of food only when you are physically hungry—we all know that most people overeat for psychological reasons—and enjoy every bite. Train hard and you will not have to spend the rest of your life looking for magic diet secrets because they just do not exist.

Food Combining

Most gastric problems, as well as weight problems, could be eliminated if people ate small meals and combined food properly. For the most part, Europeans eat only what foods are in season. They are not able to combine so many different types of food as Americans can because the foods are not available at the same

THE DIGESTIVE PROCESS

Digestion of starches (carbohydrates) begins in the mouth. The salivary glands secrete the enzyme *ptyalin*. Chewing aids such digestion.

Protein foods are broken down in the stomach by secretions of hydrochloric acid, pepsin, and gastric lipase.

The liver secretes bile, which is then stored in the gallbladder. Bile enters the duodenum from the gallbladder. The pancreas secretes the enzymes *amylase, trypsin,* and *lipase,* which enters the duodenum for digestion of starches, protein, and fat.

The small intestine is lined with projections called *villi,* which constitute the function for absorbing digested food into the body.

In 12–24 hours, all that is left of the food has reached the pelvic area for elimination through the rectum and anus.

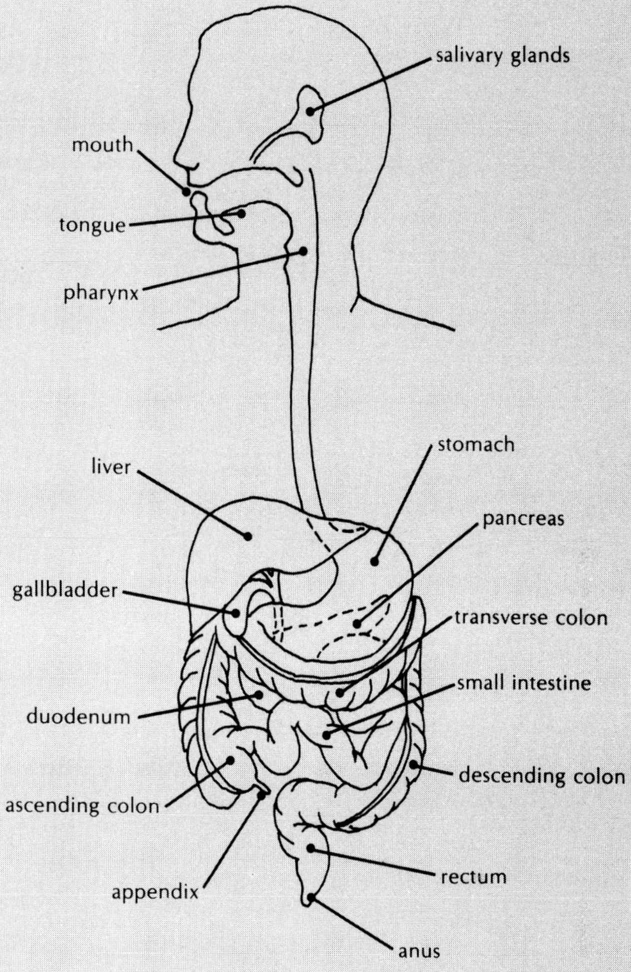

time. Let me present one more example of the typically American way of eating before I explain food combining.

Shortly after I arrived in America, Arnold told me that we were going out to lunch with some other well-known bodybuilders from the gym. Since I did not speak much English, I was happy to have lunch and get to know them outside the gym. Arnold and I met them at a smorgasbord-type restaurant. When we walked in and I saw all of this food, I thought that it was a cafeteria similar to the one that I ate in while training in Germany. There, we merely selected one or two things to eat and no more. At this restaurant, I watched the bodybuilders going through the line and coming back to the table with huge plates of food. I sat there in shock as they began to eat all of it.

When I asked Arnold (in German) if they

actually were going to eat everything, he assured me they would.

"But aren't they going to enter the contests?" I asked.

"Yes," said Arnold, "this is how they eat in America."

I completely lost my appetite just watching them wolf down all of that food as I sat there with some fish and vegetables on my plate. Arnold had little more to eat than I, but the bodybuilders kept asking him if I was sick or what was wrong. Arnold finally had to tell them that I wasn't hungry because I had eaten before I had gone to train. That certainly didn't prevent the bodybuilders from going back for desserts and ice cream!

My point is: There is no way that anyone can properly digest all the combinations of food that are served in such a restaurant. If you do go to a smorgasbord restaurant, limit your food selections and be sure to bring along plenty of enzyme supplements. You will need them.

Each enzyme is specific in its action. That is, each one acts upon only one class of food; enzymes that act upon carbohydrates do not and cannot act upon proteins or salts or fats. They are even more specific than this would indicate because there are various stages in digestion and each stage requires the action of a different enzyme. Furthermore, an enzyme is capable of performing its work only if work in the preceding stage has been properly performed by the appropriate enzymes.

Because the stomach secretes a different kind of juice when a starch food is eaten than when a protein food is eaten, carbohydrate and protein foods should be eaten separately as much as possible. Even protein foods differ enough to require modifications of the digestive juices. Protein foods in combination with other proteins and different classes of foods—even the timing of secretions—have different effects on the digestive process.

I will have more to say about enzymes later in this chapter, but what I have to say now is just that *eating is not as simple an act as you may think.* What works best is to have either vegetables with protein or vegetables with carbohydrates and not carbohydrates and proteins at the same meal. Do not combine different types of protein at the same meal and eat only such fruits as papaya, pineapple, apples, and grapes with protein foods.

Believe me when I tell you to keep your meals very simple—you will eliminate any digestive problems you may have as well as avoid digestive problems in the future. If you are still hungry after your simple meal, then wait an hour or two and have another small meal. If you allow yourself the time to digest your food efficiently, you will not have problems overeating even if you eat five or six times a day.

Follow my example and you can't go wrong. (You should consult your doctor about allergies, which are most likely a result of improper food combining anyway.) In the morning, I eat three eggs over medium—cooked as little as possible. I have a dish of plain yogurt and add fresh fruit to it sometimes. The fruit must be fresh and in season, not from a can. If I have toast, I eat it together with the eggs, but not before. If I train in the morning, I wait an hour before training—you shouldn't train on a full, or empty, stomach.

During lunchtime, I will have fish—a big serving—and either eat a salad with the fish together or have the salad after eating the fish to make sure the hydrochloric acid (HCl) breaks down the fish. Eating the salad first wastes the little value the content of the salad has. At lunch, I can drink a beer or a glass of wine. This applies any time of the year, before or after a contest. I can follow this lunch with a snack of fruit; if I'm not competing, I might indulge myself with a slice of cheesecake.

Since I usually train in the late afternoon, I have another dish of plain yogurt, yogurt with fresh fruit, a big piece of fruit, or a piece of cheese with some fruit at around three o'clock. I will train about an hour later.

At dinner, I will have the same combination I had at lunch. If I can't get good fish, I'll have chicken (with skin removed), and if I can't get, or don't want, chicken, I'll have meat. I may have a baked potato and I can have the salad, eaten together or after. If I'm training very hard, I might have a late night snack: a small dish of yogurt, small piece of cheese, perhaps a little piece of tuna, tuna fish, or some kind of sardine. It is important not to eat a large amount of carbohydrates in the evening when your next workout is many hours away. Eat your desserts at lunchtime, never before going to bed.

I eat this way every day and make adjustments just as any active businessman must. But whenever I eat, I carefully consider what I am putting into my body. I prefer eating fruit before going to the gym because it gives me energy. I may even bring along a bag of fruit to help sustain me through a grueling workout and to restore depleted glycogen. I do not gorge myself on fruit—or on fish, yogurt, cheese, wine, or supplements. Everything in moderation, as I said before. Don't make your diet a list of "don'ts," just pay attention to what you eat to find what works for your body and what doesn't. Then *replace* what doesn't work with what works, rather than *restrict* your eating with the latest diet. A proper diet is just as much a matter of attitude as it is knowledge of nutrition.

Nevertheless, I believe the process of changing your eating habits requires a basic understanding of nutrition. What I will proceed to tell you now is all you need to know about nutrition to formulate your new diet. Coupled with hard training and a positive attitude, you will be able to become a champion with the body of a champion.

The Basic Nutrients

As I have shown, digestion and assimilation of food is of utmost importance to the maintenance of a healthy body. If we do not digest and assimilate our food properly, our bodies will not get the maximum nutritional benefits needed for growth, repair, and power. The chemical substances that food provides to the proper functioning of the body are called *nutrients*. There are six basic classes of nutrients: proteins, lipids (fats), carbohydrates, vitamins, minerals, and water. Each nutrient has a specific function in the body apart from its primary function of providing energy.

The body is made up of billions of cells and each cell contains all the nutrients it needs to sustain itself. Not all cells need the same nutrient nor do they need the same nutrients in the same proportions. They never use more than they need, however, so what isn't used and can't be stored may become toxic if not eliminated from the body within a certain amount of time. An insufficient amount of nutrients in the cells will cause them to stop functioning and die.

Let me explain what each class of nutrient does for the body and point out important principles of nutrition bodybuilders should know in relation to each class. You will be surprised that what seems to be common practice in bodybuilding circles is in opposition to nutritional principles.

Protein

In an average person, about 30 percent of the body's supply of protein is found in muscle tissue. In bodybuilders, this figure goes up to about 40–50 percent. Usually one gram of protein is required daily for every kilogram (2.2 pounds) of body weight. Bodybuilders and other athletes need more, of course, because their muscles are larger. Here is a chart for the normal recommended daily protein intake:

RECOMMENDED DAILY PROTEIN INTAKE

Children:	
between 3 and 6	50 milligrams (mg)
between 7 and 12	60–70 grams (g)
between 13 and 20	75–100 g
Adults:	
women	60–90 g
men	75–100 g

When you eat more protein, your body does not automatically secrete more HCl to help digest it. Therefore, I recommend that, if you are training to build more muscle and taking in more protein, you should take HCl and digestive enzyme supplements.

The building blocks of proteins are the *amino acids*. There are two types of amino acids: essential and nonessential. The nonessential amino acids are synthesized by the body's glands, and as the name implies, are nothing to worry about as long as the glands function properly. The essential amino acids are not synthesized by the body and must be provided through the food you eat.

The eight essential amino acids are *tryptophane, lysine, methionine, treonine, phenylalaine, leucine, isoleucine,* and *valine*. Some authorities include *histidine* and *arginine* among the essential amino acids although they are synthesized by the body in small amounts.

The classification of protein is further divided into *complete* and *incomplete* proteins. A complete protein is of high biological value, which means that it comes from something living (fish, chicken, mammal), and contains all of the essential amino acids in the right proportions needed by the body. An incomplete protein lacks one or more of the essential amino acids and is of low biological value, which means that it comes from a lower form of life (plants). With the exception of those found in soybeans, all vegetable proteins are incomplete. (Unless soybeans are soaked prior to cooking, however, they are very difficult to digest.)

One of the problems with a vegetarian diet is knowing how to combine the vegetable proteins into complete proteins. Most of the vegetarians that I have encountered (particularly through my chiropractic practice) have lacked essential amino acids in their diets. This deficiency is more noticeable in women who have been on strict vegetarian diets. After a few years on such a diet, a person will sag from the tip of the nose to the ends of the ankles. Without complete proteins in their diets, vegetarians invariably lose the *collagen* in their connective tissues that keeps the joints of the body smooth and flexible, and they lose the *elastin* which makes repairing tissue possible. Such a diet requires a lot of time and knowledge; otherwise it could be harmful to your health.

Use this list to select the type of protein you should consume:

- Eggs provide the most complete protein with only 12 percent of its protein *not* absorbed by the body.
- Fish is next with an approximate 78 percent absorption level.
- Dairy products come close behind with 76 percent.
- Meat is fourth with about 68 percent absorption level.
- Soybeans, about 48 percent absorption level.

Because I was raised on a complete diet of natural foods, everything that comes out of a jar, can, or box is artificial and I avoid eating it. I have the same feelings for protein tablets and powder. Protein powder is a dead food. In animal protein, the DNA in the cell, even when the animal is dead, is alive, unbroken. In protein powder, the DNA of the animal source used is broken down during the cooking process that takes place to make the powder. Thus, the powder is of low biological value. I believe that it should be used only for people who are extremely debilitated and cannot digest or absorb natural food, or in countries where the population is starving.

When I came to America I started taking protein powder drinks because that seemed the thing to do, and for the first time in my life I began to get fat. I could not, at first, imagine where the fat was coming from. I trained and trained, but still had a roll of fat around my waist. So I stopped taking the protein drinks—it was the only thing I was doing differently since coming from Europe—and, as you can probably guess, the fat disappeared and never returned.

If you insist on going against my sound

advice and take protein powder, be sure to mix it with water or milk. *Do not use fruit juice.* Fruit juice contains, in most cases, highly concentrated sugar and does not combine with protein during digestion. Instead of being digested, the protein will putrify in the colon and harden like stone. The same thing will happen with your protein tablets that have been coated with sugar to taste good.

If you feel that you are training hard and need more protein, then add one or two small protein meals to your diet program. Anything can be overdone, so experiment with your body and eat what feels right to you. You should have enough energy for training, but should not feel full or bloated. If you feel bloated, you are eating too much, not digesting what you are eating, or eating the wrong food combinations.

Protein and Enzymes. All enzymes are made of protein. To make enzymes, the body must have high quality protein foods. Before food can be utilized by the body, it must go through many changes that are brought about by enzymes. (We don't have to worry about which comes first, however; we just have to make sure the cycle isn't broken.) Enzymes are compounds that cause substances to be changed from one form into another. The minute we begin to eat, the enzymes go to work, taking food through the various stages of digestion and of elimination.

Without proper enzyme function, undigested foods become toxic (poisonous) to the body. For example, the digestion of carbohydrate foods begins in the mouth with the enzymes *ptyalin* and *maltase.* These enzymes are secreted by the salivary glands in the mouth—that is why it is important to thoroughly chew carbohydrate foods for proper digestion to take place.

Protein digestion begins in the stomach with hydrochloric acid (HCl). While HCl is not an enzyme, it provides the necessary medium for the major stomach enzyme, *pepsin,* to be effective in digesting protein. Some people have made the mistake of grouping HCl with other acids, such as those found in fruits or drugs, and thus, take these acids with their meal. These acids actually inhibit gastric digestion, either by destroying the pepsin or limiting its secretion. That is why I warned you not to mix protein powders with fruit juice; *the only fruits that combine with protein are papaya and pineapple* (rich in enzymes), *apples, and grapes.*

One of the first things to slow down in the body is the production of HCl. It has been estimated that at age 65 we produce 23 percent of the HCl we did at age 18. If you are properly combining food (eating proteins first, carbohydrates later) and still have digestive problems, then I recommend digestive supplements that include HCl.

The digestion of milk is aided by the enzyme *rennin,* which is not normally produced in the adult human. That is why bodybuilders who drink large quantities of milk tend to look smooth and fat. I always recommend that my patients eat yogurt in place of drinking milk. Plain, homemade yogurt is very easily digested and assimilated, and is rich in protein and calcium.

Enzymes are also found in the muscles. I have discovered two enzymes that are important for bodybuilders to know about. *Arginese* is a protein-digestive enzyme that breaks down protein found in muscles into the waste product *urea.* Urea is then eliminated from the body through urine; thus excess or worn out amino acids, created when muscles are broken down during heavy weight training, are prevented from contaminating the body. *Phosphatase* is an enzyme necessary for releasing the mechanical energy of muscles. It combines with the sugars, glucose and fructose, and with oxygen for the release of energy. Then carbon dioxide is carried away from the muscle cells when the energy is released.

Amino acids are broken down by the enzyme *amino acid oxidase* in the liver. The liver's function is to break down worn out or excess amino acids and it can actually convert these into glucose if needed. Most of the protein wastes become urea and are eliminated through the kidneys. If you overeat, you can

An abridged photo album that depicts a lifetime of vibrant health due to a natural diet and a combination of special knowledge and common sense about nutrition and exercise.

overload this process and set your digestive and eliminative systems working against you.

Fats

Lipids, or fat, makes up the largest food molecule one can eat. One gram of fat contains nine calories, whereas an equal amount of protein or of carbohydrate contains four calories. Fat is emulsified, or split up, by the bile salts from the liver and gallbladder. Digestion is then completed in the small intestine by the enzyme *lipase.*

Fat naturally occurs with protein foods and is used by the body as a carrier for the fat soluble vitamins, A, D, E, and K. Following absorption, fat is either oxidized (for energy) or stored in the body. Storage occurs in places you may be familiar with, known as fat deposits, and is present in most tissues. When needed later, fat is metabolized in the liver by bile salts stored in the gallbladder.

Fat is also necessary for hormone production, and this fact is particularly important for women. Women usually have 25–40 percent of body fat compared to men who have 15–25 percent of body fat. When a woman's body weight drops too low and her percentage of body fat goes under 10 percent, she usually stops menstruating. We have found this condition very common among female athletes who have come to us as patients. This is only one

By avoiding bulking up and cutting down, Franco has kept a youthful appearance, a positive outlook on life, and a championship body.

example of the relation between fat and hormones, but we hope it is dramatic enough to demonstrate the danger of severe dieting and overtraining.

When fats and protein are eaten together, the fat inhibits the secretion of gastric juice; hence digestion is impaired. So, although they occur together naturally, you are still well-advised to trim meats of excess fat, take the skin off of chicken, and avoid heavy sauces or fatty dressings on salads.

Cholesterol is another substance that is important for hormone production, and acts as a conductor of nerve impulses in the body. Here in America, everyone seems to be afraid of high cholesterol and, therefore, avoids foods that contain cholesterol. Eggs appear to be on this list of "dangerous" foods because they are high in cholesterol. It should be noted, however, that eggs also contain *lecithin* and this helps break the cholesterol down. Most often, the real causes of high cholesterol levels are stress and refined carbohydrates (refined sugar and white bread are examples). The body is usually capable of regulating its own cholesterol levels and always works to maintain a balance of nutrients.

People should be more concerned with triglycerides, the amount of fat in the blood. One of the most effective ways of keeping triglyceride levels low is vigorous physical exercise. I highly recommend that everyone have a complete blood study done on an annual basis so triglyceride levels as well as other problems involving nutrition can be monitored and prevented.

Carbohydrates

The main function of carbohydrates is to supply energy to the body. Some carbs are converted into *glucose* to provide immediate energy needs, some are stored as *glycogen* in the liver and muscles, and the rest are converted to fat and stored as *adipose* (fat) tissue. The main product of carbohydrate digestion is glucose and the central nervous system is entirely dependent on this glucose for energy.

What glucose is not immediately used by the central nervous system, is carried to the liver where it is converted to glycogen. The liver then changes it into a simple sugar as the body calls for it. The body can store approximately 350 grams of glycogen. A third of this total is stored in the liver and used for energy in all cellular activity of the body. The other two-thirds of the body's supply of glycogen is stored in the muscles and is used for muscular energy. It takes 48 hours to restore the full amount of glycogen after two or three hours of very hard training. That is why I don't recommend training twice a day or training every day, if you are training very hard. The body needs some time to rest and recuperate.

Glycogen cannot be stored in the nerve tissues. The central nervous system therefore needs replenishment of glucose through the consumption of carbs whether or not your workouts exhaust stored glycogen. That is why I am appalled to see so many people trying out low-carbohydrate diets.

I have never dieted in my life and am astonished at all the different diets that people try. When I first came to America, every bodybuilder I met was bulking up and then cutting down for contests. I could never understand how someone could let himself get fat and then try to reduce to build muscle. Well, now that bulking-up-and-cutting-down is not so popular, the fashionable thing is a very low- or no-carbohydrate diet.

I see several problems with this dietary philosophy. First, natural (unrefined) carbohydrates do not make you fat—*sugar,* a form of refined carbohydrates, makes you fat. Second, as I have already mentioned, the central nervous system becomes irritated when there is not enough glucose to meet its needs. Third, if the body can't get energy from its store of glycogen, which is primarily supplied by carbs, then it obtains its energy from its store of protein.

The first problem with cutting carbohydrates from your diet to avoid becoming fat is simply a misunderstanding of their nutritional value. Refined carbohydrates are so concentrated that they overload the system, which can only store so much for energy needs. The rest is converted to fat or eliminated before it becomes toxic. The carbs found in fresh fruit, for example, are not so concentrated and provide just what your body can use.

Because the nerve tissues of your body cannot store glycogen, which can be converted to the sugar needed for nervous energy by other tissues, you need to eat carbohydrate food on a regular basis to replenish energy for your nervous system. What happens to the bodybuilder on a low-carb diet is that he becomes nervous and irritable and his contest performance is affected. If he carries the diet too far, he can have a dried-up-prune look due to a lack of fat. It is one thing to look defined on stage and another to look wrinkled up.

The final problem with the low-carb

philosophy is the effect it can have on the protein level of the body. A bodybuilder needs protein to build up muscles, and an appropriate level of carbs can spare the protein level from being robbed by the body for energy use. Very simply put, this means that when bodybuilders go on a high-protein, low-carb diet, their bodies are converting the extra protein into energy instead of converting it into muscle tissue.

Summary. To summarize my discussion of nutrients so far, then, just remember that carbohydrates are the primary source of energy for the body, fats are second, and protein is third. Fats are necessary for hormone production and for carrying fat-soluble vitamins to where they are needed in the body. Protein (as well as minerals and water) is the main structural material of the body.

Vitamins and Minerals

Rather than discuss each vitamin and mineral separately, here and now, I will go over the basic needs for them in this chapter and refer you to the Appendix where each vitamin and mineral is discussed. There you will find the body's use for each vitamin and mineral along with the natural sources (foods) by which you can obtain each.

Vitamins and minerals are organic food substances that are essential for the normal metabolism of other nutrients to promote proper growth and maintenance of health. The most important factor in bodybuilding is muscle growth. Therefore, it is impossible to achieve maximum muscle growth and definition unless you adhere to a supernutritious diet along with proper vitamin and mineral supplements.

Vitamins and minerals act as catalysts, or help form catalysts, in the body; they are a part of the enzyme system and assist in essential metabolic reactions. Metabolism is the conversion of digested nutrients into building material for living tissue or energy to meet the body's needs. Metabolism occurs in two general phases that occur simultaneously: anabolism and catabolism. Anabolism involves all the chemical reactions that the nutrients undergo in the construction or building up of body chemicals and tissues, such as blood, enzymes, hormones, glycogen, and others. In other words, anabolism is the building up of protoplasm from the simpler food molecules. Catabolism is the destructive phase of metabolism: the disintegration of protoplasm or the release of potential energy. It takes place in every cell without exception, but the amount varies from one type of tissue or organ to another and according to the body's demand for energy. Muscles and certain other organs are the most metabolically active structures.

Now we know that the process of metabolism takes place in each of us; however, it is much more intense in bodybuilders. The breakdown, repair, and growth of tissue is so profound in the bodybuilder that he must supplement his diet with vitamins and minerals for these processes to take place properly.

Many people think that if they eat a well-balanced diet they will have no need for extra vitamins and minerals. This is not true. First of all, most people, including bodybuilders, know very little about proper nutrition. For example, many bodybuilders eat too much protein and do not balance it out with small amounts of fat and natural carbohydrates. To be healthy, the body must have protein, fats, and carbohydrates. The diet should be simple, and as natural as possible. Second, most of the food in this country is devitalized, having been grown on soil that is depleted of minerals. Third, most processed food contains preservatives, chemicals, and hormones which could be dangerous for our health. For these reasons everyone should supplement their diet with extra nutrients. The bodybuilder, whose metabolic processes are greatly accelerated, *must* take additional vitamin and mineral supplements.

Vitamins taken in excess of the finite amount utilized in the metabolic processes are valueless and will be excreted from the body or stored. If a person uses common sense, there will not be a problem of taking too many nutritional supplements. I definitely do not believe in taking gigantic quantities of vitamins. I also take as many chewable, and capsulized, supplements as possible for easier assimilation into the body. However, read labels because many chewable vitamins contain *sugar.* Many tablets are too hard pressed and are difficult for the body to break down for assimilation. Timed-release vitamins involve a process by which vitamins are enrobed in micropellets and combined into a special base for extended release, often taking 10-15 hours for complete absorption by the body. For information on particular vitamins and minerals see the Appendix on page 187.

I do hope that you will learn something from my research and now realize the importance of vitamins and minerals for each of us—especially bodybuilders. In my opinion bodybuilders should represent vibrant good health and in order to do this, many different aspects must be researched along with proper training methods. Proper nutrition not only prevents injuries, it also helps the body heal much faster if an injury should occur.

Water

The most important nutrient in the body is water—in fact, three-fourths of the total body weight is composed of water. It has been found that a human being can live without food for a month or longer, but only a few days without water. Water is needed for all foods, vitamins, and minerals as a solvent and for digestion; it also transports and removes all wastes, regulates body temperature, and helps prevent constipation. All bodily functions take place with the aid of water.

Eight to ten glasses of water are recommended for the average person, but during hard training and nutritional supplementation more is needed, depending on the individual. Other liquids should not be substituted for water. For example, if you drink one glass of alcohol, you need water for it to be utilized by the body. Large amounts of water while eating meals is not necessary because it can actually dilute digestive juices; however, a small amount will assist in the transport of HCl.

Glandular Supplements

During hard training, the endocrine system—which is composed of eight different glands (pituitary, thyroid, parathyroid, pancreas, suprarenal [adrenal], ovaries, testes, and pineal)—is highly stressed. The glands of the endocrine system work in harmony with the nervous system to control and coordinate all activities of the body. The substance secreted by an endocrine gland is called a hormone. The hormones pass directly into the blood through the capillaries and are taken to other parts of the body. An excess or deficiency of a particular hormone may result in a specific disease state. Once the endocrine system is out of balance, your body chemistry also is upset.

Taking glandular supplements can be very beneficial in bodybuilding, because the glands are working harder and can become depleted of their hormones. Glandular supplements are food for the glands and assist them in staying healthy. However, I do not recommend taking any supplements without a complete examination such as a blood test, hair mineral analysis, and muscle testing along with a thorough medical case history.

In addition to the structural body types (see Chapter 2 on Anatomy), four distinct glandular types of people have been described according to the gland which is inherently dominant in their body. The *adrenal type* has been described as the stereotypical workaholic, who has high energy and who usually gets the job done. The *thyroid type* is a high energy individual, usually thin and wiry. The *pituitary type* is the intellectual, and the *gonadal type* is usually earthy and comfortable in any surrounding. You should keep this in mind when selecting your glandular supplements because your lifestyle and body type are important considerations in creating a specific nutritional program.

Chapter 9

STEROIDS AND OTHER DRUGS

The human body is a complex organism that works to maintain what we call homeostasis, which is a state of equilibrium or balance. No matter what happens to the body, when one structure or organ is affected another area is also affected. We see this daily in vivid detail on spinal x-rays that have been taken in our chiropractic center. Whenever one area of the spine is out of alignment, another area has compensated for the misalignment in order for the structure to stay balanced. The more involved we become with the human body through our chiropractic practice, the more respect we have for its Creator. The human body has been perfectly created and it is a masterpiece in every way. This is why it is so difficult for us to understand how an intelligent person can continue to maintain self-destructive habits, particularly athletes who should be prime examples of excellent health.

Aside from rigid, ill-informed dieting practices, the most common problem in bodybuilding today is the taking of steroid drugs. I became a Mr. Universe winner before I knew that steroid drugs existed. I have also traveled to many of the so-called underdeveloped countries and have found excellent bodybuilders who just trained hard—some even used cement blocks because they did not have weights—and ate their regular ethnic diet. These people are great examples of what bodybuilding can do because, instead of looking for shortcuts and drugs to make them champions, they stayed with the basic concept of training hard and concentrating on healthful practices.

The most common steroid drugs that are used in bodybuilding are: dianabol, deca durabolin, winstrol, primobolan, anivar, and testosterone. Other harmful substances that are also used are: thyroid medication, diuretics, salt tablets, etc. I am amazed at what people will do to their bodies in order to look better. It is unfortunate to see so many bodybuilders willing to try any kind of tablet or injection with the hope of becoming a champion and winning the competitive edge, when in reality they are losing their health.

Steroid drugs have become so popular with athletes because they cause a temporary weight gain—which is interpreted as more size—and a temporary increase in strength so that training can be increased.

After years of experimenting with these drugs, doctors and bodybuilders have concluded that dianabol is the most effective. They have also decided that 15 mg a day should be taken for a period not longer than 8 weeks, or it becomes ineffective. All drugs should definitely be prescribed by a qualified medical doctor only after all of the necessary lab work has been completed. Even when drugs are no longer being prescribed, the lab work should continue periodically because every drug has side effects which can be disastrous. Some people can tolerate these effects more than others before actually getting into a diseased state, but no one escapes from the bad side effects.

Since the liver works to detoxify the system, it is really overworked when drugs are taken. And once the period of stress or work is lessened (e.g., when drugs have been discontinued), the liver will slow down and actually become sluggish so that it is not able to take care of its normal functioning. I would recommend that B-complex vitamins and Vitamin B-12 be increased during the period of drug taking, so the liver will continue to function more normally. Steroids cause an almost immediate calcium imbalance. This imbalance should be checked because calcium is probably the most important mineral for developing healthy muscles and bones.

The *Physician's Desk Reference* clearly states, "anabolic steroids do not enhance athletic ability." I firmly believe that drug taking among athletes should be outlawed in every type of competition. It is not possible to go into complete detail concerning each of the steroid drugs, so I have chosen to quote the *Physician's Desk Reference* on dianabol since other steroids have similar effects.

Contraindications: Hypersensitivity; male patients with carcinoma of the prostate or breast; carcinoma of the breast in some females; pregnancy, because of masculinization of the fetus; nephrosis of nephrotic phase of nephritis (kidney problems).

Adverse reactions in males: *Prepubertal:* Phallic enlargement; increased frequency of erection. *Postpubertal:* Inhibition of testicular function; oligospermia (decrease of spermatozoa in seminal fluid); gynecomastia (abnormally large mammary glands in the male; sometimes may secrete milk).

Adverse reactions in females: Hirsutism (growth of body hair); male pattern baldness; deepening of the voice; clitoral enlargement; menstrual irregularities; masculinization of the fetus.

Adverse reactions in both sexes: Increase in blood pressure; nausea; fullness; loss of appetite; vomiting; burning of the tongue; increased or decreased libido; acne (especially in females); inhibition of gonadotropin secretion; jaundice; liver dysfunction.

There is a sort of rumor among some competitive bodybuilders that steroids in tablet form pass through the liver, but injected steroids bypass the liver. This is just not so; the truth remains that NOTHING BYPASSES THE LIVER. The human body always works as a unit and this cannot be overstressed. And while we're talking about competitive bodybuilders, remember that several have died as a consequence of taking steroids—all champions, whose bodies (from outwardly appearance) would be expected to ward off side effects with ease.

Thyroid Medication

The thyroid is one of the most sensitive glands of the body. The speed of virtually all the basic cellular processes of the body is regulated largely by the thyroid gland. The thyroid hormone functions in at least 20 enzyme systems. One of the major activities of thyroxine involves the acceleration of metabolic activity. This is why thyroid tablets have become so popular among bodybuilders and among those who want to lose weight.

However, thyroid tablets are of no help to a bodybuilder because a stimulated thyroid makes you lose muscle at the same rate you lose fat. The most devastating effect of thyroid pills is that they stimulate the parathyroid gland at the same time, and the parathyroid gland controls the calcium content of the bones. Stimulated, it takes calcium out of the bones and puts it into the blood tissue. This causes a severe calcium deficiency in the bones, making them brittle. Tendons and liga-

ments attached to the bones can easily become separated. A blood test would show high calcium content in the blood, and unless the doctor knew that you were taking thyroid medication, he would tell you to stay away from calcium—just when you need it the most. The deficiency would become even worse, leading to muscle spasms and cramps in training, a decrease in performance, and much more serious injuries later.

I can always tell whether an athlete has been taking thyroid medication just by his or her behavior: extreme hyperactivity and irritability. No title or trophy is worth the price of such negative behavior—and such behavior during a contest is hardly the mark of a true champion.

Diuretics and Salt Pills

Both diuretics and salt pills upset the sodium/potassium balance of the interstitial fluid in and around body cells. Since every activity of the body takes place at cellular level, it is dangerous to use these supplements. Diuretics also cause potassium to be excreted causing a mineral imbalance and giving one a dried-up look on stage. It also makes the kidneys work much harder.

Cigarette Smoking

Listed below are *some* of the adverse reactions caused by cigarette smoking: increased likelihood of lung cancer and bladder cancer; stroke; increased serum cholesterol, triglycerides, and fatty acids; increased need for Vitamin C; loss of taste, smell, and hearing ability; decreased sexual drive; incitement of skin to wrinkle 20 years beyond chronological age (particularly for women); marked decrease in visual perception; increased likelihood of blindness; increased susceptibility to allergies, asthma, bronchitis, and emphysema; increased release rate of adrenalin; increased heart rate; increased blood pressure; initiated narrowing and thickening of arteries; cause of small spasms in coronary arteries; ventricular fibrillation (uncontrolled heart muscle contractions); and increase in possibility of heart disease.

Marijuana

Marijuana, like cigarette smoking, is being linked to more and more disease processes in the body. I cannot discuss this drug at length, but there are a few pertinent facts that I would like to present. A week after a person smokes marijuana, 30 percent of its active agents are still in the body. There is no other drug or medication that is known to linger in the body so long. Of the portion that remains, the body retains 70 percent of that longer than the second week. It gets rid of only 10 percent a month thereafter. The primary damage is in the brain and autonomic nervous system which alters all of the body controls and thinking centers. In heavy users there is atrophy of the body musculature and a corresponding atrophy in the brain. It also is known to cause more lung damage than cigarettes.

Caffeine

Caffeine is a drug. The immediate effects of caffeine begin soon after it is taken and last about four hours. These may include imperfect balance, racing of the heart, high-pitched voice, insomnia, fatigue, and finger tremor. In the long term, caffeine can raise blood pressure, cause the heart to race or have extra beats, injure the pancreas, make diabetes and hypoglycemia much worse, and cause peptic ulcers and irritability of the nervous system. Any long, continued irritation in the body can turn into a cancer by damaging the chromosome structure of the cells of the body. Birth defects and a host of other diseases have more recently been linked with caffeine.

A study was done by Loma Linda University on the measure of immunity called *the phagocyte index*. The researchers found that one 12-ounce cola drink will drop the index from

95 to 70. Anytime your immunity level drops under 70, you are susceptible to infection. However, if you take as little as 20–50 mg of Vitamin C at the same time as the cola, there will be no drop in the phagocyte index. So you can take a little poison if you take the antidote at the same time. Whole fruits have Vitamin C.

Alcohol

Drinking alcohol causes damage to the brain, heart, and liver. Drinking hastens damage to the brain by cutting off oxygen supply to enormous numbers of small areas of brain tissue, thereby prematurely killing large numbers of brain cells. Successive damage done to the brain accumulates. Brain cells do not multiply and are therefore irreplaceable. The liver and heart are forced to work harder—thus over a period of time all of the organs can become overloaded.

The more we overwork our bodies with poisons, the less efficient the body becomes and sooner or later we find ourselves in a diseased state. Drugs also have adverse reactions on mental capabilities and can completely change a person's personality. The less able a person is to cope with problems and stresses of daily life, the more difficult it becomes when that person takes drugs to mask over the symptoms.

Good nutrition and exercise create a healthy body, mind, and spirit. So many problems can be prevented if we would just take a little time each day to focus on all of the positive aspects of our life and be thankful. Each of us has the power to choose what is right for ourselves. I hope that you choose not to contaminate your body and mind with drugs and negativity. Why choose sickness when you can be vibrantly alive and enjoy every aspect of your life as a learning process?

WELCOME
FRANCO COLUMBU
WELCOME
FRANCO COLUMBU
WELCOME
FRANCO COLUMBU

Chapter 10

BODYBUILDING FOR GOOD HEALTH & LONG LIFE

All the bodybuilding programs we have discussed in this book can be applied to successful muscle development for many years. Muscle development varies from one individual to the next, of course, but it is not unusual at all for the muscles to continue to grow well into a man's late fifties. And even when a bodybuilding program does outlive its potential to stimulate muscle growth, there are still exercise routines that can be used for health and fitness for many enjoyable years.

Benefits of Training

A common misapprehension about bodybuilding is that its benefits are limited to building muscle. Let's take a final look at some good beneath-the-surface reasons for bodybuilding training.

First, bodybuilding differs from other sports in that it trains *all* body parts, not just a few. It also delivers tremendous benefits to your internal organs, such as the liver, heart, stomach, and intestines. And it is one of the best sports for enhancing blood circulation to the brain. Just about all other sports, team-oriented or otherwise, are played in a standing position, with the blood going mostly to the legs, much less to the upper body. But bodybuilding has you squatting, sitting, inclined, or supine as well, and thus your blood is dispersed to different body parts during the course of a single workout. When you bench press, for instance, there's a tremendous influx of blood to the chest and shoulders, thus to the neck, and on to the brain.

"Use it or lose it." Russian research has indicated that the brain and muscles degener-

ate the least if used the most. We all know that a muscle placed in a cast for any length of time will atrophy completely; the body probably has no worse enemy than inactivity. Bodybuilding improves muscle tone for the entire body better than any other sport. And a dedicated bodybuilder can enjoy improved skin tone because weight training brings an added blood supply to the skin.

When it comes to reducing fat, bodybuilding does a far better job than most other sports because muscle cells and fat cells simply do not mix. The first deposit of fat in the body occurs in the liver. From there it travels to the pericardium; after fat accumulates around the organs, it builds up under the skin. When fat can be seen under the skin, it's a cinch that fat cells surround the vital organs, too. So weight training, which directly reduces fat between muscle and skin, obviously reduces fat around the organs at the same time. To me, *that is the finest benefit that the sport has to offer.* You can't attach a barbell directly to your heart or your liver, of course, but a sensible weight program will promote the health of those vital organs just as surely as though you were training them directly.

Improved health habits. Training also encourages you toward better health habits. For instance, I know very few bodybuilders who smoke. Abused lungs complain quite clearly and loudly when asked to help with anything as strenuous as training with weights, thus the bodybuilder will be forced to choose between smoking and training well before he reaches advanced training levels. Similarly, training will make you feel like drinking less alcohol and eating better food and more vitamins. You will simply feel healthier inside and out.

Appearance. Your clothes will fit and look better. Men's clothes are designed with the assumption that the body which fills them will have *some* taper to it. When you enhance that taper through weight training, you enhance just what the designer of your clothes had in mind. When clothes fit and look better on you, you will take vastly increased pride in the way you look in them.

MR. OLYMPIA
1981

Competitive bodybuilders must have their clothes made, of course, because contest-sized thighs threaten the seams of most trousers, and chests and shoulders overflow the jackets that are available off the rack. When you buy a size 44 suit, for instance, the pants are normally 38 inches or so in the waist; I know men with 50-inch chests who could go swimming in size 38 pants.

A good appearance can have business benefits, too. I came to America with only a high school education and no English, but I have still made a success out of my business ventures—physique contests and seminars, appearances in television and movies, professional degrees in chiropractic and in nutrition. I believe there's a built-in attitude out there which says, "If that man takes such meticulous care of his body, he must take excellent care of business as well." And you can benefit from that attitude just as I have—without being built like I am, or even close.

Discipline. There is no question that successful bodybuilding will make you feel better about yourself. As you learn to respect your body, you learn to respect your fellow man, too. The discipline required for training will carry over to many other aspects of your life. Bodybuilders are generally more intelligent and better-educated than is popularly assumed, and I can think of at least three world-class bodybuilders who have taught or are teaching school. That is no coincidence, because the same discipline that drives you to train can drive you to learn.

Increased lifespan. It's well documented that man has the capacity to live far longer than he actually does. What holds him back is the cultivation of daily mistakes and bad habits. A cigarette smoker who maintains this filthy habit for 50 or 60 years loses about 15 years of life, if a woman, and about 20 years, if a man; that's my idea of an awesome price to pay for a questionably pleasurable habit. Alcohol, used immoderately, causes shrinking of the brain cells and nerve degeneration, plus liver problems such as cirrhosis. Even a chocolate cake or a dish of ice cream can take two or three minutes off your lifespan.

Now, worrying about the possible penalties of every mouthful you consume is a good way to drive yourself batty; a far more reasonable solution is to restrict these bad habits to only *occasional* use, so that your good habits outweigh your bad ones and an indulgence now and then poses no threat to you.

As you get older, heavy training and jerky movements become considerably more dangerous. You must strive to improve your circulation and train all body parts equally for good balance. Once your program is no longer concentrated on building muscle, concentrate instead on a steady pace and good muscle balance. Your training should feel comfortable, and your joints should bend comfortably.

Other training adjustments to be made as you get older include keeping warm throughout your workout. Wear warm training clothes, even in summer, for instance. Take more time warming up and stretching, so you feel loose before you start. Lighter weights and more repetitions will improve your circulation and help you avoid injury.

Your maximum capacity for muscle attainment occurs between the ages of 15 and 40, and within that approximate timespan, you can achieve your absolute potential within 3-5 years if you train hard and correctly for that length of time. But look at what's available to you for the rest of your life:

- From age 40 to 50, you can develop muscle to 90 percent of your potential.
- From age 50 to 60, you can develop muscle to between 65 percent and 90 percent of your potential.
- From age 60 to 70, you can achieve 40-70 percent of your potential.
- From age 70 to 80, you can achieve 20-40 percent of your potential.
- And even after age 80, you can still develop up to 20 percent of your muscle potential!

Training is the most effective means of stimulating your muscles and organs. As you stimulate your body through training, it becomes increasingly important to feed it the right food, hence our chapter on *bodybuilding* nutrition. And it's equally important to vary your training workouts for new stimulation whenever points of staleness or no improvement come along, which they surely will whether you've been a bodybuilder for months or for years. Everybody hits "sticking points" now and then, so you can count on a new training program to provide new stimulation. This is why I have included such a variety of programs in this book.

Here's a good 20-exercise weight training

program for men of 60 years or so. Do *not* attempt to complement this program with jogging! Jogging is outright dangerous at this age; bones are more brittle, lower back problems occur more frequently, and nerves are prone to degeneration. Much better by far is a routine in which you run briskly for a few blocks and then walk a few, alternating the two for a few miles. Running uphill is the most beneficial.

The emphasis of this program, remember, is on high reps and light or no weight.

ROUTINE FOR THE GOLDEN YEARS

Standing leg stretch—3 × 20. (180)
Standing side bends—3 × 20. (180)
Lunges—3 × 20, light dumbbells or no weight at all. (151)
Standing press—2 × 20. (176)
Bench press—3 × 20. (123)
Lat pulldowns—3 × 20. (158–9)
One-arm row—3 × 15. (154)
Bent-over lateral raises—4 × 15. Excellent for posture. (125–6)
Lateral raises—3 × 15. (146)
Triceps pushdowns—4 × 15. (182)
Seated dumbbell curls—3 × 10. (164–5)
Leg extensions—4 × 25. (148)
Leg curls—2 × 25. (147)
Calf raises—5 × 20. (170, 177)
Bent-leg sit-ups—4 × 25. (124)
Bent-leg raises—4 × 25. (124)
Lying side leg raises—4 × 35. (152)
Side bends—2 × 20. (168)
Leg stretch—2 × 20. (121)

My Personal Wish for You

Had I remained a shepherd or construction worker, I have no doubt that I would still be healthy and strong, with a long life expectancy. Bodybuilding has not changed me so much as it made me expand my horizons. I have traveled all over the world many times and have many accomplishments that make me recognizable to millions of strangers. I can think of no greater joy than to see their looks of recognition wherever I go. I owe it all to bodybuilding.

I wish you the best of luck in your endeavor to use the information I have provided in this book and reshape your body and your life. If you train hard, eat right, and think positively, you will succeed at every goal you set for yourself. So set those goals high and get to work—enjoy the long life that lies before you.

Exercise Glossary

Back Leg Stretch (Hamstring Stretch)

Stand and place one leg on the top of a bench or chair. Keep your knee straight and bend forward. Feel the stretching in the back of the thighs (hamstring muscles or leg biceps). This exercise must be done slowly. Do not force the stretch.

Barbell Rowing

Bend forward from the waist, use a medium width grip on the bar, palms down. Raise the bar to your chest, then lower it.

Bench Press

Lie down comfortably on a bench and keep your spine straight, grip 30–40 inches apart. Lift the barbell and straighten out your elbows. Bring the bar down to your chest and repeat.

Bent-Leg Raises

Lie flat on your back with your arms to the side or as shown in photos. Start in the straight position (below). Your feet will be slightly above the floor. Bring your knees to your chest (right), then push your legs out straight again. Do not rest your feet on the floor at any point in this exercise.

Bent-Leg Sit-ups

Lie on your back with your hands overhead (below). Bend your knees and try to bring them to your elbows, which remain straight (bottom photo). Keep your spine on the floor.

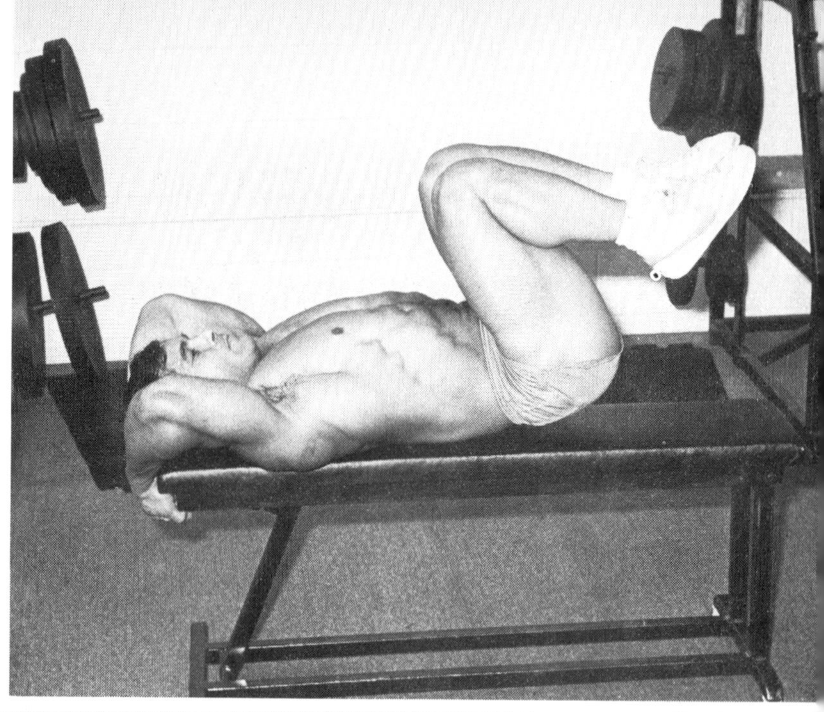

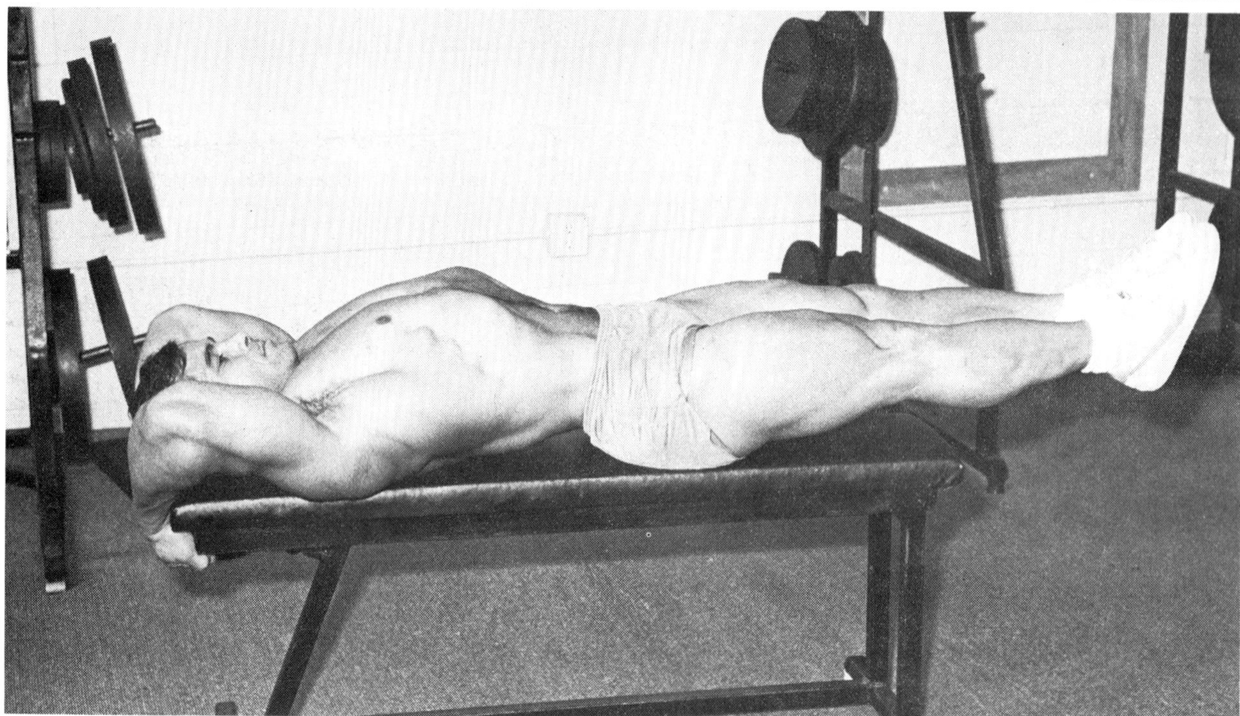

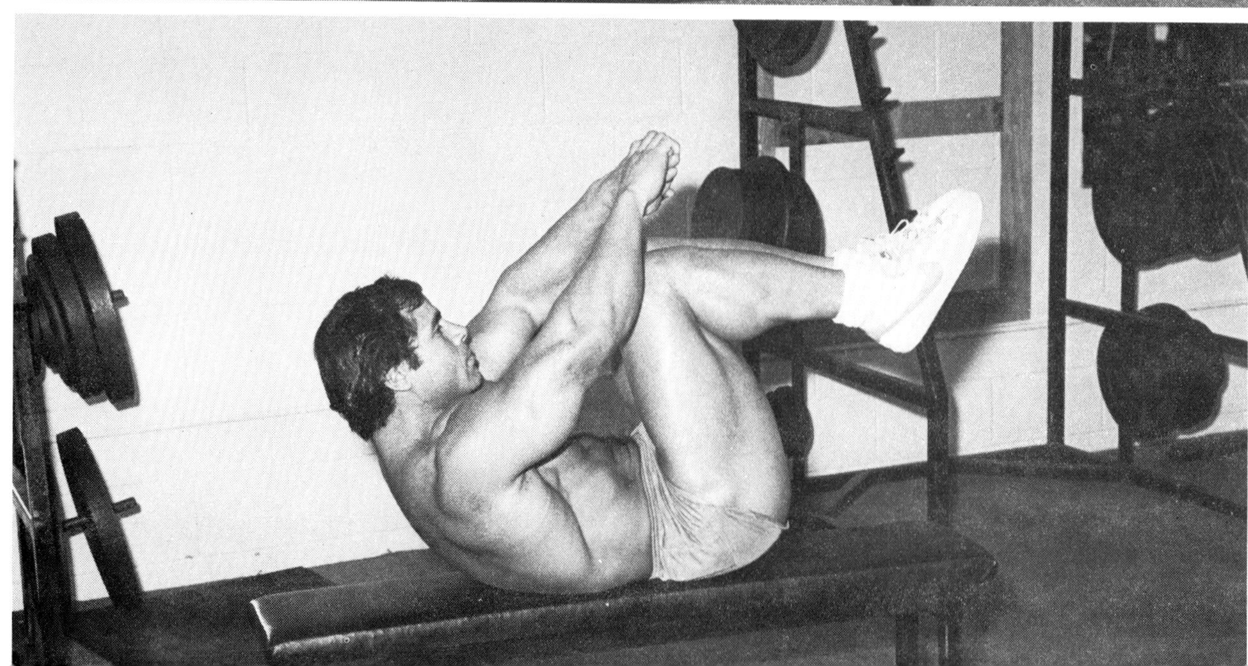

Bent-Over Lateral Raises

Sit on the edge of a bench with your knees slightly bent. Bend your upper body 30–40 degrees. With your elbows bent, lift the weight to the side as much as you can. You should feel this in the area of the back deltoid and rhomboideus muscles. This exercise may also be done in the standing position (see next page). Keep feet shoulder width apart and bend from the waist.

Between Door Presses

This exercise is like a push-up done standing up. Lean forward with both arms stretched out to the sides of a doorframe at shoulder height. Bend your arms and let your body drop through the doorway. From this extreme position, push yourself back, straightening your arms and locking out your elbows. (See photos on page 7.)

Breathing

Exhale during the exertion phase of the exercise. Example, for the bench press, inhale as you bring the weight down to your chest and exhale as you raise the weight.

Calf Stretching

Stand on a step with your foot halfway into the step, heel down, and push with your body weight, stretching the back of the calf. (See photos for Standing Calf Raises.)

Chins Behind the Neck

Use a very wide grip. Pull yourself up until the back of your neck touches the bar, then lower yourself down all the way for a good, full stretch.

Chins in Front of the Neck

Use a very wide grip, and try to pull up as high as possible. Tense your lats all the way up and down, and be sure to get a good stretch at the bottom.

Clean

Grip a barbell tightly, hands 15–20 inches apart. Keep your feet no more than 12 inches apart. Pull the weight and clean it, bringing it straight up. Bend your knees and bring one leg in front of the other for balance. Rest the bar on the front shoulders.

Clean and Jerk

As you clean the weight to your chest, stand erect and jerk the weight full power overhead fast. At the same time, split your feet apart, bringing one foot in front and one foot in back about 30-40 inches apart.

Clean and Press

As you clean the weight to your chest, stand straight. Press the weight up overhead, looking straight forward, and bring the weight back down to the chest. (Not shown.)

Concentration Curl

Spread your legs and bend your knees. Bend forward and rest your free hand on your knee, for some back support. Pick up the dumbbell, keep your arm vertical, and curl as correctly as you can.

Cross Flyes

Lie on your back on a small bench or on the floor, holding a dumbbell in each hand. From a position of arms outstretched to both sides, raise both arms straight up and cross them. Be sure to control the movement, advancing each arm equally.

Crunch Sit-ups

Lie flat on the floor with your legs resting on top of a bench or chair with knees bent. Place your hand in front of the chest, and raise your upper body close to your knees.

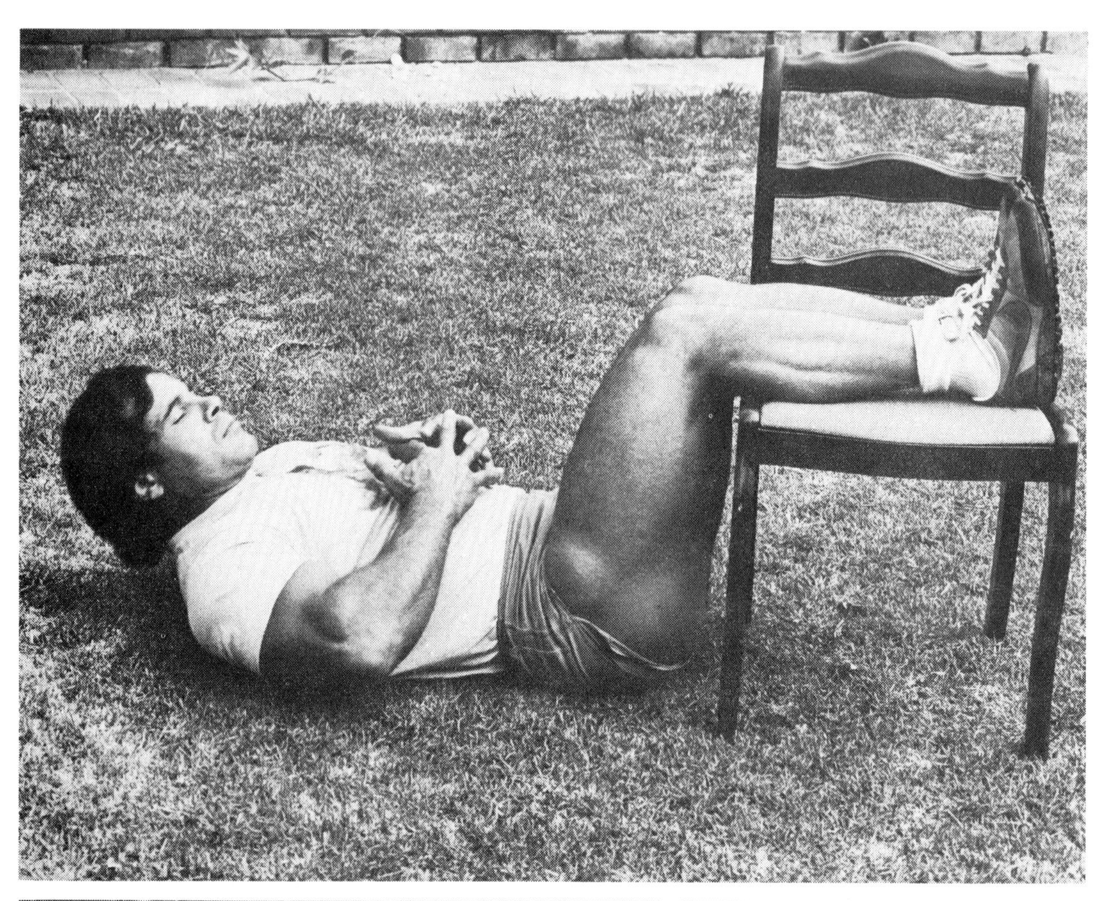

Deadlift

Grip the bar with one hand over, one hand under. You simply grip the bar as it lies on the floor, then stand erect, your arms hanging down.

Dips

Can be done on the parallel bars or on two chairs, with a tight grip. Push up and down while looking forward. Inhale and descend as low as possible, then ascend using the force of the chest, shoulders, and arms, and exhale.

Donkey Kicks

Get on your hands and knees. Keep your entire spine straight and your pelvis tilted. Bring your right knee into your chest and then extend it back up above the level of the hip. Repeat with the opposite leg.

Donkey Raises

Use a calf block. Bend over on a 45-degree angle, resting your arms on a high bench. Keep your knees straight, inhale and descend as low as you can, then rise on your toes as far as possible and exhale completely.

Flyes

This movement is done in the bent-arm style. Bend your arms as you lower the dumbbells, then return to a straight-arm starting position. Inhale deeply on the way down, exhale on the way up. Get a full stretch on each repetition.

Forward Bends

Stand with your feet comfortably apart, arms stretched straight up overhead. Bend forward from the waist, keeping your arms above your ears. Continue forward as far as you can, feeling the stretch in the back of your legs. Hold, then raise back up very slowly.

Front Calf Raises

Stand with both feet on a block of wood.
Hold onto the back of a chair for balance.
Go up and down on toes.

Front Dumbbell Raises

With a dumbbell in each hand, raise arms one at a time straight up in front above shoulder level.

Front Squat

You need a high board under your ankles for proper balance. Place the bar comfortably in front of your neck on the top of your shoulders. Try to keep your back straight; looking above your head will help. Breathe in on down, out on top.

Hamstring Stretch

See Back Leg Stretch.

Hyperextension

Lie on your stomach, absolutely flat against the bench or floor. Place your hands on the back of your neck. Have someone hold your feet from behind. Raise your head and upper body until your lower back feels tension. Release to floor or bench, and repeat. You can also do this exercise as shown in photos.

Incline Barbell Press

Start with the bar held over the eyes, inhale deeply as you lower it to just below your neck, then exhale as you push the bar back to the starting position.

Incline Dumbbell Press

Start with dumbbells held over your eyes, inhale deeply as you lower them to just below your neck, then exhale as you push the dumbbells back to the starting position.

Jumping Rope

This is one of the best conditioning exercises ever devised. The key is to learn to jump rope in many different ways such as on one foot, both feet together, slow, and fast.

Jump Squat

Hold two 5-10 lb. dumbbells. Stand with your feet 12 inches apart. Jump up and bend the knees to the chest as you are up in the air. Come back down on your toes.

Lateral Raises

Stand erect with your feet approximately 12 inches apart. Hold one dumbbell in each hand and bend your elbows slightly. Raise the dumbbells slightly higher than your shoulder level. Repeat.

Leg Curl

Lie on your stomach on the bench. Hold onto the bench to stabilize your body. Raise your chest off the bench, but keep your hips on the bench. Put the weight on the ankles, not the calves. Straighten the legs completely on the way down; try to touch your thighs on the way up. Action must be fluid, without jerking.

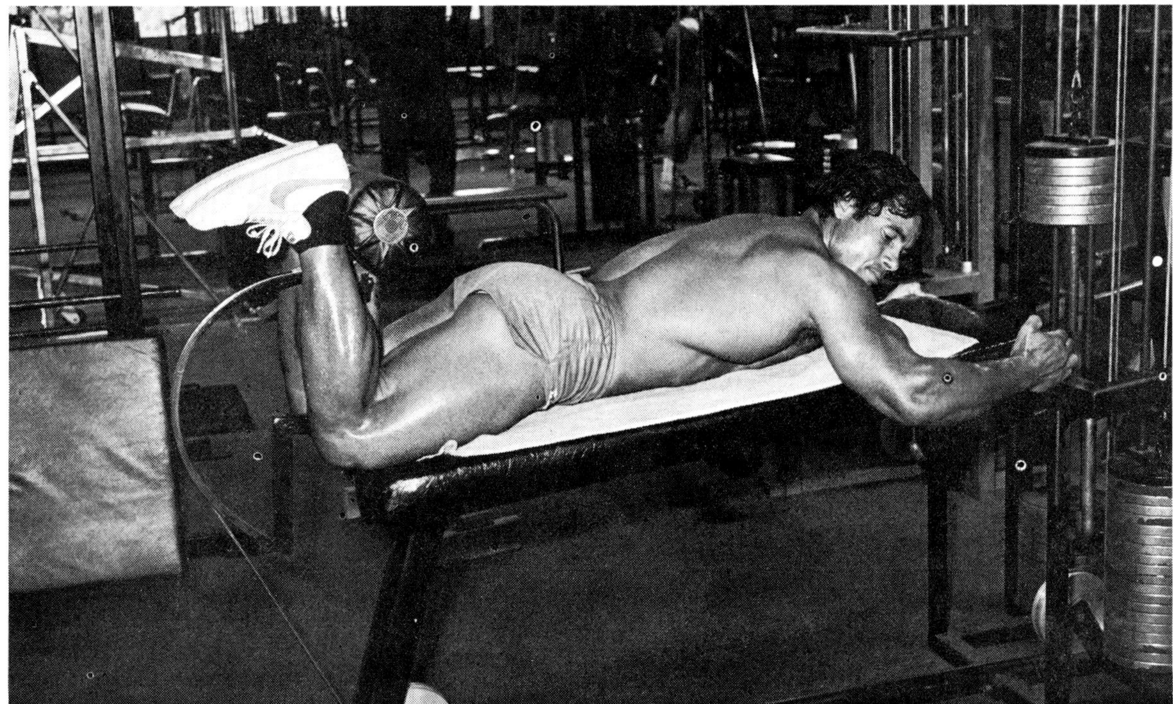

Leg Extension

Begin seated on a bench or sturdy chair. Place your hands on hips or hold onto the bench. Put weight on your ankles. Extend legs straight on the way up, bending them on the way down.

Leg Press

Sit and press the pedals of the leg press. Use your whole foot or only your toes, whichever feels more comfortable. Breathe out as you push.

Leg Raises

Lie flat on your back on the floor or on a bench. Keep hands straight down at your side or as shown in photos. Raise both legs together straight up, flexing your knees and pointing your toes. Don't move your hips from the bench.

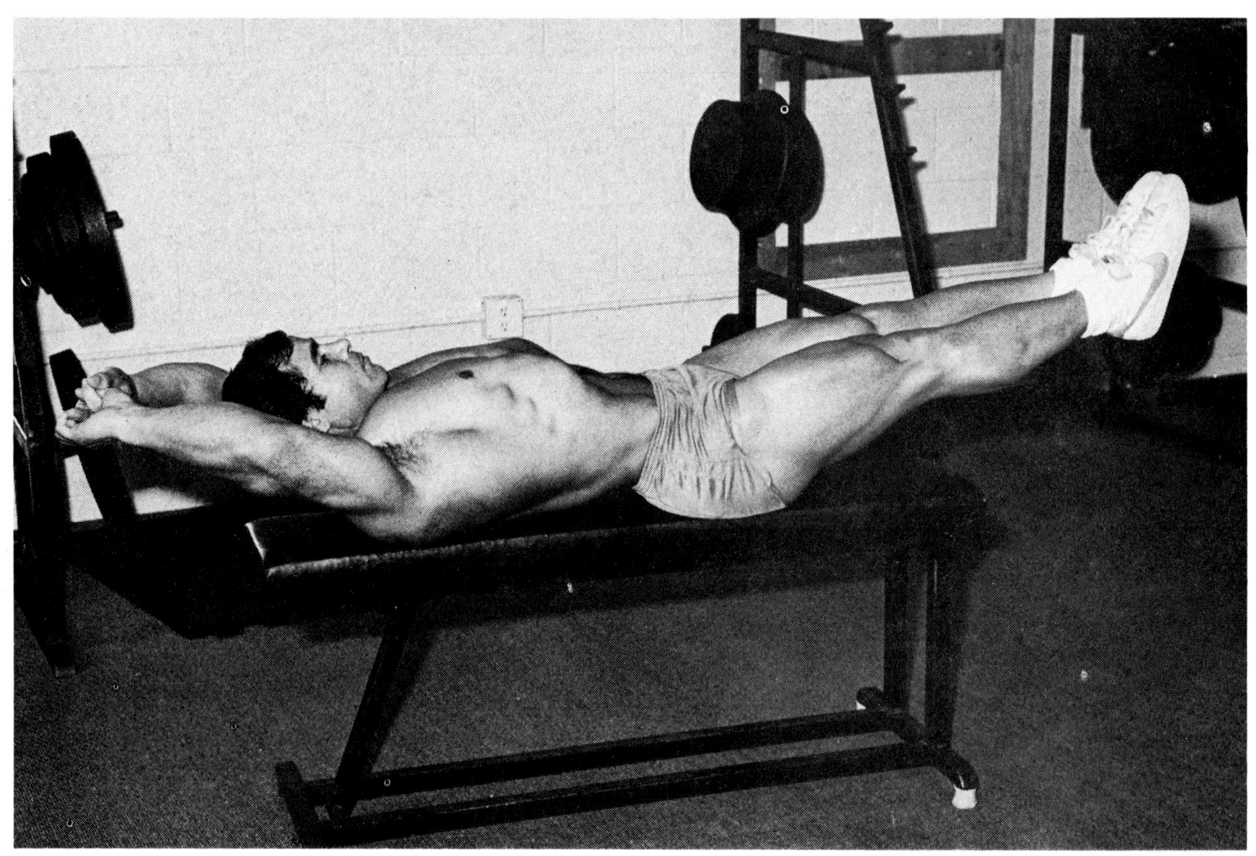

Lunges

Stand up straight with a weight in each hand or the barbell across your shoulders. Step forward as far as you can on your left foot. As you step forward, lower your body; your right knee will almost touch the floor. Raise, stand up straight again, and put your right foot forward to repeat the lunge phase of this exercise. Hold your head and torso straight throughout the exercise.

Lying Side Leg Raises

Lie on your left side with your legs straight. Place your right arm in front of you, support your head with the left. Raise your left leg to its maximum height for the required number of reps. Turn on your right side and raise your right leg in the same way.

Lying Triceps Extension

Lie down on the bench, point your elbows straight up, lower the bar to your forehead, then press it out for a complete extension. Don't move your elbows. (Shown above.)

Narrow-Grip Bench Press

Lie down on a bench. Grip the bar, hands 4–6 inches apart. As you bring the bar down, inhale and lock your elbows out. Your hands should touch your chest and then push up with full force. Exhale, bringing the arms to a full extension. (Shown below.)

One-Arm Rowing

Hold a dumbbell in one hand, just off the floor, between your legs. Your body should be bent at a right angle to the floor. Pull the dumbbell up till it touches the side of your pectoral muscles, then lower all the way down for that full stretch.

One-Arm Triceps Extension

Use one dumbbell. You can stand straight or sit down holding the dumbbell with one hand. Keep the upper arm straight up and as you bend the arm, inhale; as you straighten the arm, exhale.

Preacher's Bench

Grasp the barbell about 10–14 inches apart. Hands facing up from straight down, curl the barbell up to your chin then extend your arms. Elbows should be 10–14 inches apart.

Press Behind the Neck

Use a medium-wide grip. Sit down, inhale, lower the bar to the base of your neck, then quickly press it overhead while exhaling. Perform your reps without pausing. Keep your back straight—preferably braced—for this exercise.

Pulldowns/Behind Neck

Kneeling on the floor, take the weight bar behind your neck and pull it down as far as you can. Raise. Pull down. Repeat. Exhale as you pull down.

Pulldowns/Front Neck

Kneeling on the floor, pull the weight bar from its top position to the upper chest. Raise. Pull down. Repeat.

Pulley Rowing

Usually the pulley is a few inches off the floor. Sit down in front and grab the pulley handles. Keep your knees straight and pull to the chest and then bring the hands from the chest outward.

Pullovers

Lie on a bench or across a chair, and hold a dumbbell or barbell overhead with slightly bent arms. If you use a barbell, grip it no wider than your shoulders. Slowly lower the weight behind your head, inhaling as you lower the weight and exhaling as you return to the starting position. The important thing here is to get a good stretch.

Push-ups

Lie flat on your stomach with your legs straight, palms flat on the floor about even with your shoulder. Push up and then lower your body. This can also be done between two chairs to get more extension.

Reverse Wrist Curl

Use either "E-Z curl" bar or a barbell. Start with your arms supported by a bench or other flat surface. Grip hands over barbell, keep the elbows still and straight. Curl your wrists up and down.

Running

Warm up well. Take small steps using a gliding motion. For the best workout, run up and down hills. But don't overdo it, letting three miles be your maximum distance.

Running in Place

Land lightly on your toes. As you continue running, lift your knees higher. This can also be done on a trampoline or running machine.

Seated Dumbbell Curls

Hold a dumbbell in each hand. Curl the dumbbells upward. As you curl turn your wrists outward, then lower the dumbbell.

120
120

Seated Stretch

Sit comfortably with your legs spread as wide as you can. Stretch your right hand to the opposite foot, left hand to the right foot and so on.

Shrugs

You can use a barbell or two dumbbells. Keep hands and arms down and shrug with your trapezius muscles moving the shoulders.

Side Bends

Stand erect with your hands on your hips and your feet spread wide apart. Bend equally to the right and then to the left.

Sitting Barbell Triceps Extension

Sit on an incline bench and hold a barbell, with hands 10–12 inches apart, behind your head. Raise and lower the barbell as low as possible for the best stretch you can get. This exercise may also be done standing.

Sitting Calf Raises

If you do not have access to a calf machine you can use a barbell. Sit on a bench and use a calf block. Place the bar on top of your thighs and hold it with your hands while raising and lowering your feet as much as possible.

Sit-ups

Lie down on an abdominal board or the floor with your knees bent as much as possible to prevent lower back problems. Place your hands in front of your chest or as shown in photos and raise your body with your abdominal muscles. Do not place your hands behind your neck and lift with your neck. This causes neck injuries. To get extra stress, you can do sit-ups on an incline.

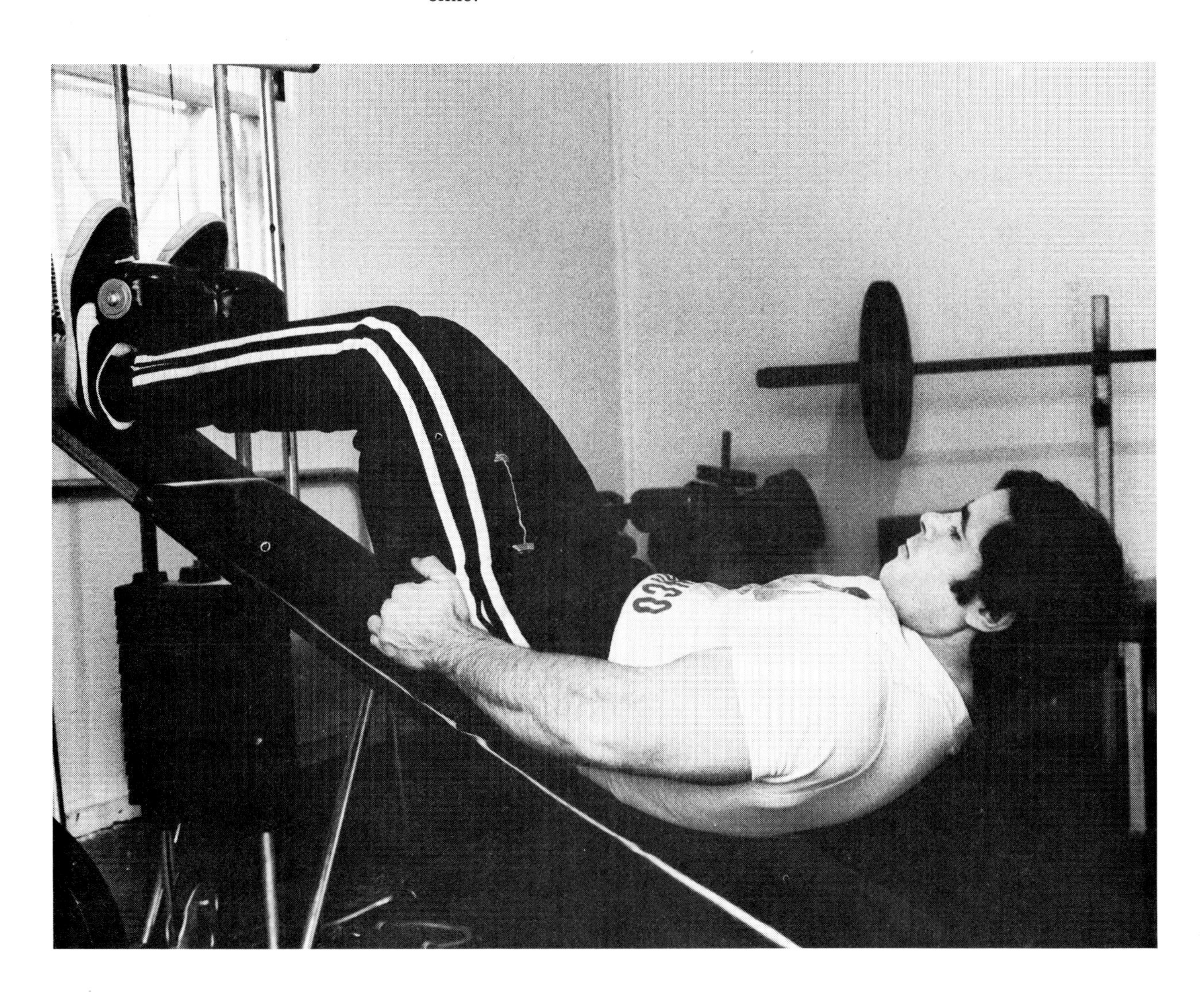

Snatch

Stand erect with your feet close together. Grip a barbell with a wide grip. Lift the barbell all the way up in one move and at the same time spread your legs one in front of the other. Keep the weight straight overhead and stand straight with your feet 12 inches apart. The snatch is completed.

Squat

Stand with a book or a two-inch block of wood under your heels with your feet approximately 12 inches apart. Bend down slowly into a full squat, keeping control of the movement. Slowly stand.

Standing Barbell Curl

Start with your arms straight down, holding the barbell. Curl the bar while keeping the arms in. The upper body may rock very slightly. Squeeze the bar.

Standing Barbell Press

Clean the barbell to your shoulders using a regular grip (about shoulder width). Exhale as you push the weight up overhead, and inhale as you lower the weight back to the starting position.

Standing Calf Raises

Stand with one foot on a block of wood. Hold onto the back of a chair for balance. Go up and down on toes. Change legs. This helps to shape skinny calves or to firm flabby ones. (You can also stretch both calves at the same time as shown.)

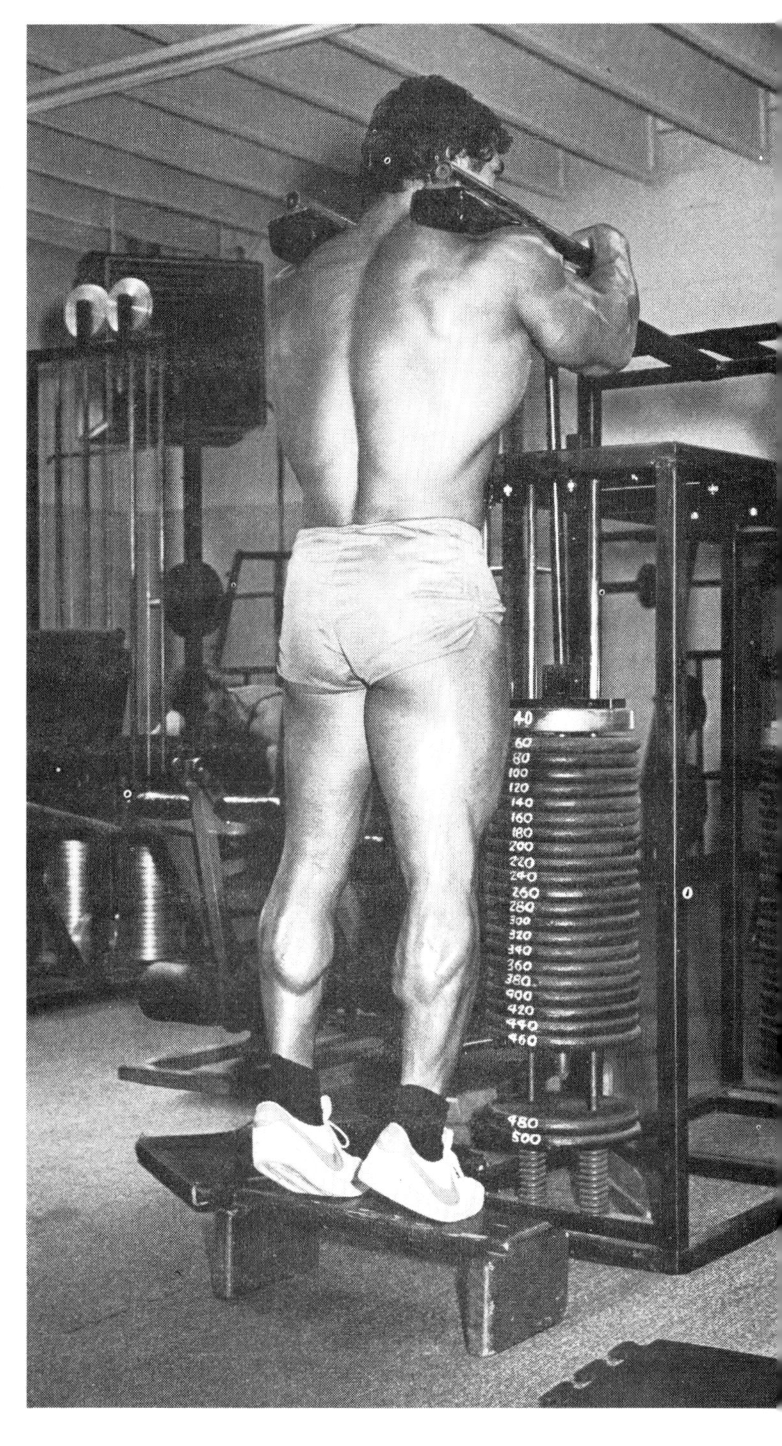

Standing Dumbbell Curl

Stand on a bench with a dumbbell in each hand. Turn your palms inward toward your body and as you curl upward turn your palms facing up. Lower the dumbbells to the starting position and repeat.

Standing Dumbbell Press

From floor, clean the dumbbell to your shoulders using a regular grip (about shoulder width), hold, then exhale as you push the weight up overhead, and inhale as you lower the dumbbell back to the starting position.

Standing Forearm Flexion Extension

Stand erect, holding a dumbbell in each arm with your palms inward. Move your hands outward and inward, and feel both sides of the forearm muscles moving.

Standing Leg Stretch

Stand about 40 inches back and face the wall. Lean forward, stretch out arms and support your body with your hands against the wall. Keep back straight, head up, and hips and legs locked. Keep your feet flat on the floor. Inhale as you raise up on your right toes as high as possible. Hold, then return to starting position and exhale. Inhale and raise up on your left toes as high as possible, hold, and return to starting position and exhale.

Standing Side Bends

See Side Bends.

Straight Leg Deadlift

Grip the bar with one hand over and one hand under, then stand erect with your arms hanging down.

T-Bar Rowing

Stand with your feet approximately 15 inches apart. Bend from the waist, keep your knees slightly bent. Grab one end of a T-bar or barbell and pull it toward your stomach with a smooth movement. Lower it to full extension and repeat. Do not jerk the bar.

Triceps Extension

See Sitting Barbell Triceps Extension.

Triceps Pushdown

Use a close grip, and bend forward slightly. Push the bar down until your arms are straight. Exhale as you push down and do all your reps with one continuous motion.

Triceps Push-ups

This exercise can be done on the floor or between two chairs. Place your hands approximately 15–20 inches apart. Keep your arms and legs straight and push up and down.

Upright Rowing

Use overhand grip to pick up the barbell, with hands spaced 6 inches apart. Pull the bar up to your chin and lower it to thigh level again. Pull up and inhale, lower and exhale.

70

Weight Boxing

Hold one dumbbell in each hand and box in front of a mirror. This will increase your punch power and strengthen the muscles that you use to hold your gloves.

Wrist Curl

Start with your arms supported by a bench or other flat surface, such as a stool. Keep the elbows still and straight. Curl your wrists upward.

Appendix

VITAMINS AND MINERALS

There has been an explosive growth in specialty stores serving people's nutritional needs. Vitamins and minerals are packaged in a wide variety of ways, so it will be important for you to read the labels. Look for supplements that are labeled "High potency," "No artificial color," "No sugar," "No preservatives," and "Timed-release." Check over the combination and amounts of each vitamin and mineral as well as ascertaining the date of expiration.

Before actually spending money on vitamin and mineral supplements, it is advisable to have two tests taken: a complete blood study and hair mineral analysis. Have a professional interpret the test results for you and work out your food supplement program accordingly.

Now I will go into specific detail regarding the known and estimated functions of vitamins and minerals. I will also list the best natural sources of each nutrient. Always try to get your nutrients from their natural sources as much as possible.

Vitamins

Vitamins are broken into two groups on the basis of solubility. The fat soluble vitamins (A, D, and E) are found in foods containing a high percentage of lipids. The water soluble vitamins (B-complex and C) cannot be stored by the body and require constant replenishment.

Fat Soluble Vitamins

Vitamin A—Best natural sources: Fish, liver, oil, eggs, and dairy products. Vitamin A

- Builds resistance to infection, especially of the respiratory tract;
- Helps maintain a healthy condition of the outer layers of many tissues and organs;
- Promotes growth and vitality;
- Permits formation of visual purple in the eye, which counteracts night blindness and weak eyesight; and
- Promotes healthy skin.

Vitamin D—Best natural sources: Dairy products, fish, and fish liver oils. Vitamin D is best utilized when taken with Vitamin A. It regulates the use of calcium and phosphorus in the body and, therefore, is necessary for the proper formation of teeth and bones. Because of this relationship with calcium and phosphorus, Vitamin D is valuable in maintaining a stable nervous system, normal heart action, and normal blood clotting.

Vitamin E—Best natural sources: Eggs, wheat germ, vegetable oils, soybeans, Brussels sprouts, spinach, leafy greens, and whole wheat. This vitamin is extremely important for the bodybuilder because it plays an essential role in cellular respiration of all muscles, especially cardiac and skeletal muscles. Vitamin E also

- Makes it possible for cardiac and skeletal muscles and nerves to function with less oxygen, thereby increasing their endurance and stamina;
- Causes dilation of the blood vessels, permitting a fuller flow of blood to the heart;
- Inhibits blood coagulation;
- Aids in bringing nourishment to cells, strengthening the capillary walls, and protecting red blood cells from destruction by environmental poisons;
- Aids in preventing aging and lowering blood pressure;
- Prevents elevated scar formation on the surface of the body as well as within; and
- Has a dramatic effect on the reproductive organs, helping prevent miscarriages, increasing fertility, and restoring male potency.

Water Soluble Vitamins

Vitamin C (ascorbic acid)—Best natural sources: Berries and citrus fruits. This vitamin is a great aid in bodybuilding because it helps the body warm up faster and thins out the synovial fluids that lubricate the joints, causing freer movement when exercising. Vitamin C also

- Maintains the body's stores of *collagen,* a protein necessary for the formation of connective tissue in skin, ligaments, and bones;
- Plays a role in healing wounds and burns by facilitating the formation of connective tissue in scars and of red blood cells to prevent hemorrhaging;
- Fights bacterial infections and reduces the effects of some allergy-producing substances (hence, its use in preventing and treating the common cold); and
- Fulfills increased requirements of tissue for ascorbic acid under conditions of increased metabolism and stress.

B-Complex Vitamins

The following ten vitamins are the most important of the B-complex group. They should always be taken together; otherwise certain deficiencies could result.

Vitamin B-17 (laetrile)—Best natural sources: Whole kernels of apricots, plums, cherries, peaches, nectarines, and apples. This vitamin is very popular in Europe, and very controversial in the United States. It is most commonly produced from the apricot pit. Claims have been made that laetrile has cancer-controlling properties.

Vitamin B-1 (thiamine)—Best natural sources:

Liver, heart, kidney, yeast, eggs, nuts, berries, legumes, green leafy vegetables, and whole grain cereals. Vitamin B-1

- Promotes and aids growth and digestion;
- Is essential for normal functioning of nerve tissues, muscles, and the heart; and
- Aids in the metabolism of carbohydrates and fats.

Vitamin B-2 (riboflavin)—Best natural sources: Milk, liver, fish, eggs, yeast, and some green vegetables. Vitamin B-2 is essential for healthy eyes, skin, and mouth. It also

- Improves growth and promotes general health;
- Helps eliminate sores in the mouth and lips; and
- Helps metabolize proteins, fats, and carbohydrates.

Vitamin B-6 (pyridoxine)—Best natural sources: Eggs, beef, milk, brewers' yeast, bran, wheat germ, liver, heart, and cabbage. This vitamin is a great help to many bodybuilders who need to prevent water retention before competition, because it is a natural diuretic. Pharmacological diuretics can cause chemical imbalances and are very damaging to the kidneys. Vitamin B-6 also

- Aids in the metabolism of proteins and fats;
- Ensures proper synthesis of amino acids and aids food assimilation; and
- Prevents nausea and various nerve and skin disorders.

Pantothenic acid—Best natural sources: Most meats, liver, heart, kidneys, nuts, whole grains, and green vegetables. A correlation between pantothenic acid levels in tissue and the functioning of the adrenal cortex indicates that this vitamin can improve the body's ability to withstand the stressful conditions brought about by hard training. Pantothenic acid also

- Prevents fatigue; and
- Helps in the building of body cells, in maintaining normal skin tone, and in the growth and development of the central nervous system.

Folic acid—Best natural sources: Most vegetables and egg yolk. Folic acid is important to bodybuilders because it stimulates the production of HCl (hydrochloric acid), which is needed to digest protein. It also

- Aids in protein metabolism;
- Contributes to normal growth; and
- Is essential to the formation of red blood cells through its action on bone marrow.

Choline—Best natural sources: Egg yolks, yeast, liver, wheat germ, heart, and green vegetables. Choline is necessary for normal metabolism because it regulates the function of the liver, minimizing excess fat deposits in the liver. It also has been shown to prevent memory loss.

Inositol—Best natural sources: Liver, brewers' yeast, and most vegetables. Inositol performs similar functions to those of choline and has been found to be helpful in brain cell nutrition. It also

- Helps lower cholesterol levels in the blood; and
- Prevents thinning hair and baldness.

Vitamin B-12 (cobalomin)—Best natural sources: Liver, eggs, cheese, milk, beef, and kidneys. This vitamin helps in the formation and regeneration of red blood cells and plays an essential role in metabolizing protein, fat, and carbohydrates.

Biotin—Best natural sources: Liver, heart, kidneys, egg yolk, peanuts, filberts, mushrooms, and cauliflower. Biotin is a factor in promoting growth and is possible related to the metabolism of fat and the conversion of certain amino acids.

Vitamin B-15 (pangamic acid)—Best natural sources: Grains, pumpkin seeds, brewers' yeast, sesame seeds, and brown rice. This vitamin has been used extensively on Russian athletes for increasing energy. Vitamin B-15

- Promotes protein metabolism, particularly in the heart muscles; and
- Regulates fat and sugar metabolism.

Minerals

I am quite sure that one of the reasons for my extraordinary strength is the mineral-rich diet I had while growing up in Sardinia. Unless minerals are present in the body, vitamins cannot do their work. Minerals are needed for overall mental and physical functioning. To ensure more complete assimilation of minerals by the body, look for chelated minerals, which are 10 times more digestible than nonchelated minerals.

Calcium—Best natural sources: Dairy products, fish, chicken, meat, whole grains, wheat germ, bran, kidneys, liver, heart, nuts, brewers' yeast, and some green vegetables. Calcium should be increased according to how much you train—every hour of training, you need an average 1,000 mg of extra calcium. Every time you get cramps, increase your calcium intake. Calcium

- Plays an important part in muscle growth, muscle contraction, and nerve transmission;
- Builds and maintains bones and teeth;
- Helps blood to clot;
- Regulates heart rhythm;
- Aids vitality and endurance; and
- Decreases the propensity for irritability, nervousness, and insomnia.

Phosphorus—Best natural sources: All natural foods. Calcium and phosphorus must exist in a 2.5/1 ratio in the body. *White sugar foods interfere with this delicate balance.* Phosphorus plays a part in almost every chemical reaction within the body because it is present in every cell. Phosphorus

- Converts oxidative energy into cell work and is interrelated with the action of calcium and Vitamin D;
- Influences protein, carbohydrate, and fat synthesis in the form of high energy phosphates;
- Stimulates muscular contraction, secretion of glandular hormones, nerve impulses (in conjuction with calcium), and kidney function;
- Neutralizes blood acidity;
- Helps create *lecithin* and *cerebrin*—ingredients needed for mental power;
- Metabolizes fats and starches (carbohydrates); and
- Is needed for normal bone and tooth structure.

Iron—Best natural sources: Meats, liver, heart, kidneys, brain, eggs, nuts, oysters, asparagus, and beans. Iron is required in the manufacture of hemoglobin and of myoglobin, which is found only in muscle tissue and which helps transport oxygen in muscle cells for use in chemical reactions that result in muscle contractions. Iron also helps carry oxygen in the blood.

Copper—Best natural sources: Seafoods and beans. This mineral is present in many enzymes that break down or build up body tissue. It is also required for the manufacture of hemoglobin and for carrying oxygen in the blood.

Magnesium—Best natural sources: Fruits, nuts, and seeds. Along with calcium, magnesium is vital for any athlete because both help prevent muscle cramps. Magnesium also

- Helps convert blood sugar into energy;
- Is required for calcium and Vitamin C metabolism;
- Is essential for normal functioning of the nervous and muscular systems; and
- Plays an important role as a coenzyme in the building of proteins.

Sulphur—Best natural sources: Fish, eggs, beef, and beans. Sulphur works with the B-complex vitamins that are needed for metabolism and for strong nerve health. It also

- Is vital for good skin, hair, and nails;
- Works to cause the liver to secrete bile;
- Maintains overall body balance; and
- Influences brain function.

Manganese—Best natural sources: Egg yolks, nuts, and green, leafy vegetables. This mineral works with other minerals to create normal bone structure. Manganese also

- Helps activate enzymes for proper digestion and utilization of food;
- Aids in muscular reflexes; and
- Helps eliminate fatigue and nervous irritability.

Sodium—Best natural source: Table salt. The main purpose of sodium is to render other blood minerals more soluble and to prevent them from becoming clogged or deposited in the blood distribution system. Sodium also

- Provides strength to the muscles so they can contract;
- Works with potassium to help maintain a favorable acid-base factor;
- Maintains a normal water level balance between cells and fluids;
- Enables the nerves to respond to stimulation and to transmit it; and
- Joins with choline to improve blood and lymph health.

Potassium—Best natural sources: Potatoes, bananas, vegetables, and seeds. Potassium joins with phosphorus to send oxygen to the brain and works with sodium to normalize heartbeat and feed the muscular system. It also is necessary for normal muscle tone, heart action, and enzyme reactions.

Chlorine—Best natural source: Table salt. This mineral serves two very important functions for the bodybuilder by keeping a youthful joint-and-tendon condition and by helping the distribution of hormones secreted by the endocrine glands. It also

- Cleans out toxic waste products from the system; and
- Stimulates the production of HCl (hydrochloric acid), which is needed for digestion.

Iodine—Best natural sources: Seafoods, vegetables, and kelp—not table salt. Iodine plays an important role in regulating the body's production of energy and in the proper functioning of the thyroid gland, upon which mentality, speech, and the condition of hair, skin, and teeth are dependent. It also

- Promotes growth and development; and
- Stimulates the rate of metabolism, helping the body burn off excess fat.

Zinc—Best natural sources: Meat and eggs. Zinc is one of the most important minerals in bodybuilding and supplementation will be a must because very little is found in most natural foods due to soil depletion. It is necessary for the normal absorption of vitamins, especially B-complex. Zinc also

- Is essential for general growth, the proper development of the reproductive organs, and the normal functioning of the prostate gland;
- Produces energy;
- Plays an important role in healing burns and wounds;
- Helps in the synthesis of proteins; and
- Governs controllability in muscles.

Recommendations

Each of us is completely different in our chemical make-up and lifestyle. Therefore, it is nearly impossible to give exact recommendations for which quantities of vitamins and minerals will be best for you. I try to teach each of my patients to work out their own nutritional program according to how they feel. You have to take time to tune in to your body and work out your own diet and supplement program.

Below is a chart with supplement guidelines for an average person, a noncompetitive bodybuilder or a person not under a lot of stress, and a competitive bodybuilder. When under stress our nutrient requirement is higher because the body is using nutrients rapidly. Enzymes also are inhibited by negative emotions such as anger, worry, fear, fatigue, etc. For this reason it is better not to eat when on an emotional high or low. Relax first and eat later.

Suggested Daily Intake	Average	Noncompetition	Competition
Vitamin A	25,000 IU	30,000 IU	50,000 IU
Vitamin D	400 IU	400 IU	400 IU
Vitamin C	1,000 mg	2,000 mg	3–4,000 mg
Vitamin E	1,000 IU	1,000 IU	1,500 IU
Vitamin B-1	100 mg	150 mg	150 mg
Vitamin B-2	100 mg	150 mg	150 mg
Vitamin B-6	150 mg	200 mg	300 mg
Vitamin B-12	300 mcg	300 mcg	500 mcg
Niacin or niacinamide	100 mg	150 mg	200 mg
Pantothenic acid	100 mg	300 mg	500 mg
Para-amino-benzoic acid	75 mg	100 mg	200 mg
Choline	100 mg	200 mg	500 mg
Inositol	100 mg	200 mg	300 mg
Folic acid	400 mcg	400 mcg	400 mcg
Biotin	100 mcg	100 mcg	100 mcg
Calcium	1,000 mg	2,000 mg	3,000 mg
Magnesium	500 mg	1,000 mg	1,500 mg
Potassium	200 mg	500 mg	600–1,000 mg
Phosphorus	150 mg	150 mg	150 mg
Iron	20 mg	20 mg	20 mg
Iodine	20 mg	20 mg	20 mg
Copper	2 mg	2 mg	2 mg
Zinc	25 mg	50 mg	100 mg
Manganese	20 mg	40 mg	80 mg
Chromium	750 mcg	750 mcg	750 mcg
Selenium	100 mcg	100 mcg	100 mcg
Beatine HCl	100 mg	200 mg	300 mg
Pepsin	50 mg	100 mg	100 mg
Bromelain	50 mg	50 mg	50 mg
Ox bile	30 mg	30 mg	30 mg
Pancreas substance	100 mg	200 mg	250 mg
Papain	50 mg	100 mg	150 mg
Protease	100 mg	150 mg	300 mg
Amylase	25 mg	50 mg	50 mg
Lipase	25 mg	50 mg	50 mg

Index

T

U

V

W

Z